MW01077738

PRINCIPLES OF QUALITY COSTS

PRINCIPLES OF QUALITY COSTS

Financial Measures for
Strategic Implementation
of Quality Management

FOURTH EDITION

Douglas C. Wood, editor

Sponsored by the American Society for Quality
Quality Management Division

ASQ Quality Press
Milwaukee, Wisconsin

American Society for Quality, Quality Press, Milwaukee, WI 53203
© 2013 by ASQ
All rights reserved. Published 2013.
Printed in the United States of America.

19 18 17 16   8 7 6 5 4 3

Library of Congress Cataloging-in-Publication Data

Principles of quality costs: financial measures for strategic implementation of quality management/Douglas C. Wood, editor; sponsored by the American Society for Quality, Quality Management Division.
     pages cm
Includes bibliographical references and index.
ISBN 978-0-87389-849-2 (hardcover: alk. paper)
1. Quality control—Costs. 2. Quality of products—Cost effectiveness. I. Wood, Douglas C., 1955–editor.
TS156.P6945 2012
658.4'013—dc23

                    2012042217

Publisher: William A. Tony
Acquisitions Editor: Matt T. Meinholz
Project Editor: Paul Daniel O'Mara
Production Administrator: Randall Benson

ASQ Mission: The American Society for Quality advances individual, organizational, and community excellence worldwide through learning, quality improvement, and knowledge exchange.

Attention Bookstores, Wholesalers, Schools, and Corporations: ASQ Quality Press books, video, audio, and software are available at quantity discounts with bulk purchases for business, educational, or instructional use. For information, please contact ASQ Quality Press at 800-248-1946, or write to ASQ Quality Press, P.O. Box 3005, Milwaukee, WI 53201-3005.

To place orders or to request ASQ membership information, call 800-248-1946. Visit our Web site at www.asq.org/quality-press.

♾ Printed on acid-free paper

Quality Press
600 N. Plankinton Ave.
Milwaukee, WI 53203-2914
E-mail: authors@asq.org

The Global Voice of Quality™

*Dedicated to those who believe in quality as a process
and seek to make it a cultural legacy.*

Table of Contents

List of Figures and Tables

Foreword

Knowing cost of quality is critical for managing the business and prioritizing improvements. This text is a long-awaited new perspective on the cost of quality. It is an updated approach on the financial impact of quality compared to the third edition of *The Principles of Quality Costs*, edited by Jack Campanella and the ASQ Quality Costs Committee. The ASQ Quality Management Division (QMD) was the host of the Quality Costs committee for many years. As a long-time member and past Chair of the Division, I have benefitted from my association with the experts in quality costs. As such an expert, Doug Wood provides excellent new ideas on the use of quality costs and the importance of financial measurements for organizational improvement.

I am particularly pleased to see this text published. I used the previous QMD text, *Principles of Quality Costs*, when I taught a Cost of Quality class in an undergraduate quality curriculum. Using cost of quality as a guide for process and organizational improvement is a powerful tool for both manufacturing and service. I do not use cost of quality as a standalone process improvement approach, however. I see cost of quality as an entry point for focusing on promising areas to reduce defects, address customer requirements, and maximize financial business flows. It is the first line of defense for maximizing our ability to beat the competition. Once target areas for improvement are identified by a cost of quality study, a number of process improvement and redesign models available to implement the solutions are identified.

The language of money is essential at the customer-facing boundaries of the business. Without the ability to tie action to financial outcomes, executive leadership is blind. Understanding cost of quality gives us the vision we need to integrate processes effectively to meet customer requirements and to balance our contribution to the value chain that keeps the global economy functioning.

Take full advantage of the techniques shared in this new perspective on cost of quality. It is a powerful tool and one we desperately need to succeed in the competitive marketplace of today.

– *Grace L. Duffy*
  ASQ Fellow, Past Chair, Quality Management Division
  Tavares, Florida

Preface

The last decade has seen wide changes in how quality standards are applied in industry. We now have two functions: quality assurance and process improvement. Quality assurance focuses primarily on product quality, while process improvement focuses on process quality; the principles of quality costs support both.

Improvement is everywhere, often implemented on a project basis. Unfortunately, a comprehensive cost-of-quality matrix is rarely used. Each project contains its own cost structure, and comprehensive strategic planning almost never uses the principles of quality costs.

The concepts involved in cost of quality may be somewhat better defined in larger industrial firms today than in 1999, when the prior edition of this book was published. The data on this are murky. In July 2009 the Chartered Institute of Management Accountants completed a survey titled "Management Accounting Tools for Today and Tomorrow." More than 100 tools were included, and the 439 worldwide respondents represented manufacturing and service areas. Organizations were fairly evenly distributed in size, ranging from 50 employees to more than 10,000 employees. Quality costs were one of 14 costing tools; on average, an organization was found to use 4 of these 14. Surprisingly, quality costs were used by less than 10% of respondents. Of the 14, only "throughput costing" and "kaizen costing" were used by a smaller fraction of the respondents than quality costing.

In spite of this low level of acceptance, we believe quality costing is the best tool to strategically guide improvement efforts. All strategic planning is done in currency. If the planning and control of process improvement is not done in this way, programs will wither each time there is a change in leadership.

The purpose of this book remains the same as the third edition: to provide a basic understanding of the principles of quality cost. Using this book, organizations can develop and implement a quality cost system to fit their needs. Used as an adjunct to overall financial management, these principles will help maintain vital quality improvement programs over extended timeframes.

– *Douglas C. Wood*

Acknowledgments

As a product of ASQ's Quality Management Division, this book was truly a team effort containing inputs and articles submitted and reviewed by the experts who make up its membership, both past and present. The editor would like to thank the following individuals for their contributions to this work.

FOR NEW MATERIAL

- Sandford Liebesman—for the entirely revised material in ISO 9000.
- Daniel J. Zrymiak—for much material in the software cost of quality section.
- Hugh Daughtrey—for materials completing the software cost of quality section.
- Jd Marhevko—for general review and updates of things my eye just didn't see.
- Gary Cokins—for the activity-based costing updates as well as helpful material on making the case to use this technique.
- Roderick Munro—for updates to the automotive standards.

FOR PREVIOUS MATERIAL

In addition to new material, this fourth edition uses information from many of ASQ's previous publications on the subject. The books and the editors for each of these publications are listed below. Individual contributions are included within each of the publications themselves and, although not repeated here, are no less appreciated. These contributors, as well as the editors, are acknowledged and sincerely appreciated.

- *Principles of Quality Costs* (third edition)—Jack Campanella
- *Principles of Quality Costs* (second edition)—Jack Campanella

- *Principles of Quality Costs* (first edition)—John T. Hagan
- *Guide for Reducing Quality Costs*—W.N. Moore
- *Guide for Managing Supplier Quality Costs*—William O. Winchell

Many prior contributors have built a strong foundation for this work. They include: Joan Alliger, Chuck Aubrey, Dennis Beecroft, Frank M. Gryna, Dan Houston, J. Bert Keats, Herb Krasner, April King, Nick Shepherd, Jim Robison, and John Schottmiller.

I would like to make a personal thank you to those who have provided encouragement to me: Jack Campanella, Jonathan Andell, Dennis Arter, Bill Denney, Duke Okes, Russ Westcott, and Jennifer Winchester.

Finally, thank you to my family, local and distributed. Providing seen and unseen support helped make it possible to get this work done: Marilyn, Jennifer, Christopher, and Richard.

Chapter 1

Quality Cost Concepts

HISTORY OF QUALITY COST DEVELOPMENT

One of the earliest writings pertaining to the general concept of quality costs can be found in Dr. J. M. Juran's first *Quality Control Handbook* (McGraw-Hill, 1951). Chapter 1, "The Economics of Quality," contained Dr. Juran's famous analogy of "gold in the mine." Most other papers and articles of that time dealt with more narrow economic applications. Among the earliest articles on quality cost systems as we know them today are W. J. Masser's 1957 article, "The Quality Manager and Quality Costs," Harold Freeman's 1960 paper, "How to Put Quality Costs to Use," and Chapter 5 of Dr. A. V. Feigenbaum's classic book, *Total Quality Control* (McGraw-Hill, 1961). These writings were among the first to classify quality costs according to today's familiar categories of prevention, appraisal, and failure.

In December 1963, the U.S. Department of Defense issued MIL-Q-9858A, Quality Program Requirements, making controlling costs related to quality a requirement for many government contractors and sub-contractors. This document helped to focus attention on the importance of quality cost measurements, but provided only a general approach to implementation and use. It did, however, serve to elevate interest in the subject of quality costs.

With the continued international popularity of the ISO series of standards, the concept of quality costs plays an important role as a quality improvement tool and a measure of quality management.

The ASQ Quality Costs Committee was formed in 1961 to dramatize the magnitude and importance of product quality to the well-being of a manufacturing business through measurements of the cost of quality. In 1967, the committee published *Quality Costs—What and How* to detail what should be contained in a quality cost program and to provide definitions for categories and elements of quality costs. This popular document was the best seller of any ASQ publication until its successors, *Principles of Quality Costs*, first and second editions, were published and sold even more.

The ASQ Quality Costs Committee progressed from these initial efforts to become the recognized authority for the promotion and use of quality cost systems. In addition to sponsoring professional training programs and annual new presentations on the subject, this committee has also published *Guide for*

Reducing Quality Costs, Guide for Managing Supplier Quality Costs, and *Quality Costs: Ideas and Applications,* volumes 1 and 2.

In 1983, the Quality Costs Committee joined the ASQ Quality Management Division (formerly the Administrative Applications Division) to become one of the Division's most active and productive committees.

Today it is easier than ever before to measure quality costs. Better data processing applications and more highly skilled employees allow a depth of measurement previously deemed too expensive. Today, if you do not count at least your scrap and rework costs, you are flying blind. Some firms have created sophisticated quality cost programs and profit from them on an ongoing basis. Almost all quality management consultants have quality cost programs as an integral part of their repertoire. Service industries are undergoing more in-depth scrutiny by consumer and regulatory groups questioning the validity of price or rate hikes. In these times, a clear understanding of the economics of quality and the use of a quality cost system in support of quality improvement efforts and the management of quality may make the difference between the status quo and beating the competition.

Since the previous edition of this book was published in 1999, the ASQ Quality Costs Committee has been discontinued, although the Quality Management Division still promotes the body of knowledge and adds to it as changes are needed. This field has matured and the rate of change has slowed, but these materials are no less valuable. Many newer firms have not applied this approach, and they suffer for it.

According to a study conducted in July 2009, less than 10% of firms analyze quality costs[1] and it is not a lack of tools and methods that prevents wider use: another study[2] revealed that the major reason for not tracking cost of quality was lack of management interest and support. In this study, many indicated that they believe the added effort does not provide sufficient value. A secondary reason given was the lack of adequate accounting and computer systems. With current data processing tools (automated data collection, data warehousing, data mining, and ABC system costing), this is a lame excuse. As for the value of cost-of–quality analysis, it is precisely the tool to make quality issues strategic. Strategy does not rely on analysis of parts-per-million metrics or percent satisfied customers. It uses currency, dollars and cents in U.S. terms, to plan and control the critical next steps of an organization.

Since 1999 the term *cost of poor quality* has sometimes been used as equivalent to *quality costs.* It is not equivalent, in that it only covers a portion of quality costs. Because prevention and sometimes appraisal, other components of quality costs, provide the investment to remove the cost of poor quality, organizations that only measure the "poor" costs are limited in their ability to focus on the right areas.

The wide application of various process improvement approaches such as Six Sigma and Lean has reduced quality costs and these approaches usually call out management of quality costs as a small contributor to their success. This may have it backward, however. The use of quality costing in the larger organization, along with prevention and appraisal costs, allows the right improvement projects to be selected.

THE ECONOMICS OF QUALITY — A MANAGEMENT PHILOSOPHY

As an expression, "the economics of quality" has contributed to some confusion surrounding the true business and economic value of quality management. There are those who believe there is no "economics of quality," that it is never economical to ignore quality. At the other extreme are those managers who believe it is uneconomical to have 100% quality. These managers feel free to make arbitrary decisions about the needed quality of product or service, usually expressed by the term "that's good enough." While it might appear that either of these attitudes could create a problem for management, the real dilemma occurs when many managers, supposedly working together, operate with varying degrees of these divergent views on quality. This situation will guarantee that quality never achieves its optimum role in the accomplishment of business objectives.

Because of its direct relationship to the economics of quality, regardless of how one views it, the "cost of quality" is another term that has inadvertently created confusion. Among the key points emerging from the National Conference for Quality (1982) was the idea that "cost of quality" should never be used because quality is profitable, not costly[3]. Some individuals, including H. J. Harrington[4] and Frank M. Gryna[5] colleagues, label it "poor quality cost," or the "cost of poor quality." This text will continue to refer to it as "quality costs" or the "cost of quality," since these terms remain the most familiar and widely used. Whatever it is called, it must be remembered that the cost of quality includes more than just the cost of the quality organization.

To set the record straight from the beginning, let's state two facts about quality management and the cost of quality: The real value of a quality program is determined by its ability to contribute to customer satisfaction and to profits. Cost-of-quality techniques are a tool used by management in its pursuit of quality improvement and profit contributions.

To develop the concept of quality costs, it is necessary to establish a clear picture of the difference between quality costs and the cost of the quality organization. It is important that we don't view the expenses of the quality function as quality costs. Fundamentally, every time work is redone, the cost of quality increases. Obvious examples are the reworking of a manufactured item, the re-testing of an assembly, the rebuilding of a tool, or the correction of a bank statement. Other examples may be less obvious, such as the repurchasing of defective material, the response to customer complaints, or the redesign of a faulty component. In service organizations, an obvious example is the reworking of a service—reprocessing a loan application or replacing a food order. In short, any cost that would not have been expended if quality were perfect contributes to the cost of quality.

Almost any company function can be responsible for mistakes of omission or commission that cause the redoing of work already accomplished. This is the essence of the failure costs of quality.

Scrap and *rework* are common terms in manufacturing and are expected in many companies. Although the terms are different, the same phenomenon occurs in the service sector. For example, insurance policies are rewritten, garments are exchanged or repaired, meals are returned to the kitchen, baggage is lost, and hotel rooms are not ready. In other words, a failure equivalent exists for service companies—that portion of operating costs caused by nonconformance to performance standards.

Formal quality management for service companies is a direct result of the realization that quality is the major factor in maintaining and increasing the all-important customer base. A comprehensive quality management program starts with management's understanding and support. Whether for a manufacturing or a service company, the program includes the establishment of performance standards in each area of the operation, the monitoring of actual performance, corrective action as required, and continuous quality improvement.

Whether for manufacturing or service, a quality cost program will lend credence to the business value of the quality management program and provide cost justification for the corrective actions demanded. Quality cost measurements provide guidance to the quality management program, much as the cost accounting system does for general management. It defines and quantifies those costs that are directly affected, both positively and negatively, by the quality management program, thus allowing quality to be managed more effectively.

Simply stated, quality costs are a measure of the costs specifically associated with the achievement or non achievement of product or service quality—including all product or service requirements established by the company and its contracts with customers and society. Requirements include marketing specifications, end-product and process specifications, purchase orders, engineering drawings, company procedures, operating instructions, professional or industry standards, government regulations, and any other document or customer needs that can affect the definition of product or service. More specifically, quality costs are the total of the cost incurred by (a) investing in the prevention of nonconformance to requirements; (b) appraising a product or service for conformance to requirements; and (c) failure to meet requirements. *Quality costs represent the difference between the actual cost of a product or service and what the reduced cost would be if there were no possibility of substandard service, product failure, or manufacturing defects.*

The most common format for categorizing quality costs is the Prevention–Appraisal–Failure (PAF) model. The categories in this model are shown in Figure 1.

Prevention Costs	Failure Costs
The costs of all activities specifically designed to prevent poor quality in products or services. Examples include the costs of new product review, quality planning, supplier capability surveys, process capability evaluations, quality improvement team meetings, quality improvement projects, quality education, and training.	Costs resulting from products or services not conforming to requirements or customer/user needs. Failure costs fall into internal and external categories.
	Internal Failure Costs Failure costs occurring prior to delivery or shipment of the product or the furnishing of a service to the customer. Examples include the costs of scrap, rework, reinspection, retesting, material review, and downgrading.
Appraisal Costs Costs associated with measuring, evaluating, or auditing products or services to assure conformance to quality standards and performance requirements. Examples include the costs of incoming and source inspection/ test; product, process, or service audits; calibration of measuring and test equipment; and the costs associated supplies and materials.	**External Failure Costs** Failure costs occurring after delivery or shipment of the product and during or after furnishing of a service to the customer. Examples include the costs of processing customer complaints, customer returns, warranty claims, and product recalls.

Total Quality Costs

The sum of the above costs, representing the difference between the actual cost of a product or service and what the reduced cost would be if there were no possibility of substandard service, product failure, or manufacturing defects.

Figure 1.1   Quality costs—general description.

Although it is rare that a company would go so far as to identify quality costs down to the level of an employee correcting an e-mail reply sent via cell phone, every company lives with significant elements of cost that fit this description. Unfortunately, significant chunks of quality cost are often overlooked or unrecognized simply because most accounting systems are not designed to identify them. As this is generally the case, it is not difficult to understand why most top management is more sensitive to overall cost and schedule than to quality. The interrelationship of quality, schedule, and cost is likely to be unbalanced in favor of schedule and cost—and often unwittingly at the expense of quality. This imbalance will continue to exist as long as the real cost of quality remains hidden among total costs. In fact, such a condition can easily set the stage for a still greater imbalance whenever the rising, but hidden, true cost of quality grows to a magnitude that can significantly affect a company's competitive position. We can refer to these hidden costs as a "hidden factory," since they represent cost and resources devoted to production that remain invisible to management and to the customer. This hidden factory reduces our capacity and limits our ability to respond to customer demands.

When the cost of quality rises without constraint or is tolerated at too high a level, failure to expose the condition ultimately becomes a sign of ineffective management. Yet, it is entirely possible for this condition to exist without top management's awareness. A quality cost program can warn against oncoming dangerous quality-related financial situations. An argument for needed quality improvement is always weak when it must deal in generalities and opinions, but it becomes unmistakably clear when a company suddenly finds itself in serious, costly quality trouble. It is highly probable that most failed companies had excessive but well-hidden quality costs. Even profitable companies that measure quality costs for the first time are often shocked at what they find.

To prevent being passed over by strong quality and price competition or, in a positive sense, to constantly improve your quality and cost position, it's necessary to manage quality in all aspects of company operations. To enhance the ability to manage quality, implement a quality cost system. Quality cost systems were created for this purpose.

On the premise that any dollar expenditure that could have been avoided will have a direct negative effect on profit, the value of clearly identifying the cost of quality should be obvious. Achieving this clarity of identification, however, is more easily said than done. A real danger lies in finding and collecting only a small portion of the costs involved and thinking that those represent the total. There are as many ways to hide costs in industry as there are people with imagination. This is an all too natural phenomenon in organizations that are never fully charged with inefficiencies—because some inefficiencies are hidden and not measured—and thus are able to maintain an illusion of effective management. In this kind of industrial organization, departments that cause inefficiencies in areas besides their own frequently get off scot-free because the problems they create, and their responsibility for them, are never properly identified. The costs of handling such problems are buried in the same way that other real quality costs are buried—as an accepted cost of doing business. If top management had all the facts, it would demand the measurement and control of significant quality costs.

Each identified quality performance problem carries with it a tangible recovery cost that can be assigned a value. This is the essence of quality cost measurement. In some cases, however, the value of the intangible costs entailed may transcend the pure economics of the situation. For example, what is the cost of missing an important milestone in a schedule? Quality problems are more often at fault here than other problems. But the most important of all intangible quality costs is the impact of quality problems and schedule delays on the company's performance image in the eyes of its customers—with all of its implications for the profit picture and the company's future.

It's difficult, if not impossible, to place a dollar value on the effect of intangible, often "hidden," quality costs. (See page 12 for a discussion of Taguchi's Quality Loss Function for approximation of hidden losses.) Some companies, however, have found a "multiplier effect" between measured failure costs and true failure costs. Westinghouse Electric Corporation, for example, reported that "…experience indicates that a multiplier effect of at least three or four is directly related to such hidden effects of quality failure.[6]" Figure 1.2 compares true failure costs to an iceberg; the more commonly measured failure costs adjust the tip of the iceberg. The bulk of failure costs are hidden below the surface and often are responsible for sinking the ship.

The negative effect on profit resulting from product or service of less than acceptable quality or from ineffective quality management is almost always dynamic. Once started, it mushrooms until ultimately the company finds itself in serious financial difficulties due to the two-pronged impact of an unheeded increase in quality costs coupled with a declining performance image. Management that clearly understands this also understands the economics of quality. Fortunately, a ready-made prescription awaits its decision—effective utilization of a forceful quality management and improvement program, fully supported by a quality cost system.

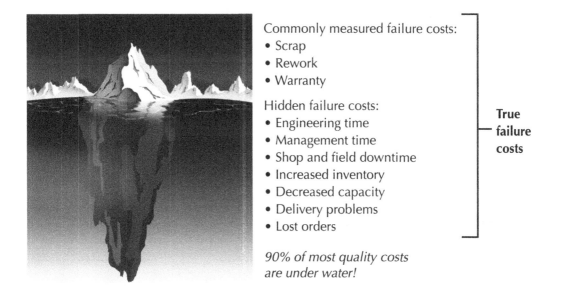

Figure 1.2   Hidden costs of quality and the multiplier effect.

GOAL OF A QUALITY COST SYSTEM

As illustrated in Figure 1.3, the most costly condition occurs when a customer finds defects. Had the manufacturer or service organization found the defects—through inspection, testing, or checking—a less costly condition would have resulted. If the manufacturing or service organization's quality program had been geared toward defect prevention and continuous quality improvement, defects and their resulting costs would have been minimized— obviously the most desirable condition. For new processes, this built-in cost of quality is avoided by using an approach such as design for Six Sigma (DFSS), also known as Define, Measure, Analyze, Design, Verify (DMADV).

Recent successes have resulted in revisions to the classic model of optimum quality costs. Previously, prevention and appraisal costs were portrayed as rising asymptotically as defect-free levels are achieved (see Figure 1.4). There is strong evidence that the processes of improvement and new loss prevention are, in themselves, subject to increasing cost effectiveness. New technology has reduced inherent failure rates of materials and products, while robotics and other forms of automation have reduced human error during production, and automated inspection and testing have reduced the human error of appraisal. These developments have resulted in an ability to achieve perfection at finite costs (see Figure 1.5).

The core concept here is that more spending in the prevention area results in lower spending in failure costs; lowered spending in prevention drives higher failure costs (otherwise known as cost of poor quality, or COPQ.) To date, the authors have found no companies where prevention and failure costs correspond on a 1-to-1 basis. The usual finding is an 8-to-1 ratio, a significant return on investment.

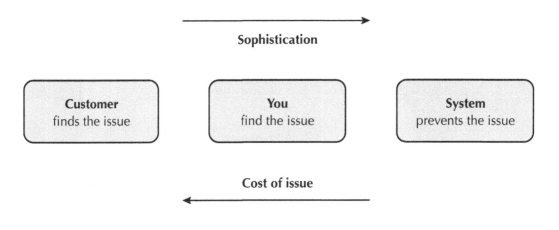

Figure 1.3   Comparative cost of quality and quality system sophistication.

Adapted by Douglas C. Wood from "Principles of Quality Costs" by Jack Campanella and Frank J. Corcoran. In *Annual Quality Congress Transactions*. Milwaukee: American Society for Quality Control, 1952.

The goal of any quality cost system, therefore, is to facilitate quality improvement efforts that will lead to operating cost reduction opportunities. The strategy for using quality costs is quite simple: (1) take direct attack on failure costs in an attempt to drive them to zero; (2) invest in the "right" prevention activities to bring about improvement; (3) reduce appraisal costs according to results achieved; and (4) continuously evaluate and redirect prevention efforts to gain further improvement.

This strategy is based on the premise that:

- For each failure there is a *root cause*

- Causes are *preventable*

- Prevention is always *cheaper*

In a practical sense, real quality costs can be measured and then reduced through the proper analysis of cause and effect. As failures are revealed through appraisal actions or customer complaints, they are examined for root causes and eliminated through corrective action. Elimination of root causes means permanent removal. The further along in the operating process a failure is discovered (that is, the nearer to product or service use by the customer), the more expensive it is to correct.

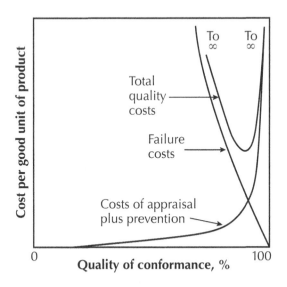

Figure 1.4   Older model of optimum quality costs.

Reproduced from Juran's *Quality Control Handbook,* 4th ed. by J.M. Juran and Frank M. Gryna. New York: McGraw-Hill Book Co., 1988.

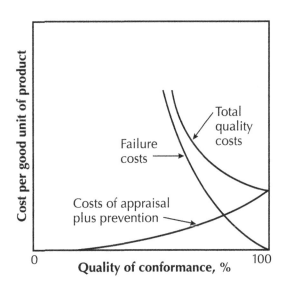

Figure 1.5 Current model of optimum quality costs.

Source: Reproduced with permission from Juran's *Quality Control Handbook,* 5th ed. by J.M. Juran, A. Blanton Godfrey, and Frank M. Gryna. New York: McGraw-Hill, 1999.

Figure 1.6 is an illustration of this concept taken from manufacturing. The concept applies to service and healthcare as well. Usually, as failure costs are reduced, appraisal efforts can also be reduced in a statistically sound manner. The knowledge gained from this improvement can then be applied, through prevention activities or disciplines, to all new work.

As straightforward as this approach may appear, it cannot work unless there is first a basic quality measurement system that clearly identifies the correctable elements of performance failures that represent the best potential for cost improvement. Such a system is designed to use the data as a measure of company performance and a resource for determining cost reduction projects. The data can come from a number of sources:

- Inspections
- Tests
- Process control measurements
- Evaluations
- Quality audits
- Customer complaints

This measurement is a basic and important part of quality management. The potential for improvement can be determined by a system of accurate and dependable quality cost measurement and analysis.

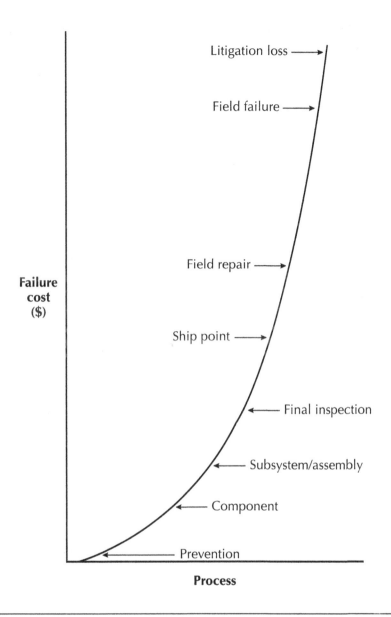

Figure 1.6 Failure cost as a function of detection point in a process.

Since every dollar of quality cost saved can have a positive effect on profit, the value of clearly identifying and using quality costs should be obvious. By minimizing quality costs, quality performance levels can be improved.

THE TAGUCHI QUALITY LOSS FUNCTION (QLF) AND THE HIDDEN COSTS OF QUALITY[7]

Dr. Genichi Taguchi developed Taguchi Methods—combined engineering and statistical methods that achieve rapid improvements in cost and quality by optimizing product design and manufacturing processes. Taguchi Methods are both a philosophy and a collection of tools used to carry forth that philosophy. Taguchi's philosophy can be summed up by the following statements:

1. We cannot reduce cost without affecting quality.

2. We can improve quality without increasing cost.

3. We can reduce cost by improving quality.

4. We can reduce cost by reducing variation. When we do so, performance and quality will automatically improve.

Taguchi disagreed with the "conformance to specification limits" approach to quality. The difference between a product barely within specification limits and a product barely out of specification limits is small, yet one is considered "good" and the other "bad." Rather, Taguchi Methods strive for minimal variation around target values without adding cost.

Taguchi defined quality as "the loss imparted to society from the time the product is shipped." Fundamental to this approach to quality engineering is this concept of loss. When we think of loss to society, things that come to mind include air pollution or excessive noise from a car with a defective muffler. Taguchi viewed loss to society on a much broader scale. He associated loss with every product that meets the consumer's hand. This loss includes, among other things, consumer dissatisfaction, added warranty costs to the producer, and loss due to a company's bad reputation, which leads to eventual loss of market share.

The idea of minimizing loss to society is somewhat abstract and thus difficult to deal with as a company objective. When we consider loss to society to be long-term loss to our company, however (and the two are equivalent), the definition may have more meaning.

The concept of "social responsibility" has gained interest in the past 10 years. In the words of ISO:

> "In the wake of increasing globalization, we have become increasingly conscious not only of what we buy, but also how the goods and services we buy have been produced. Environmentally harmful production, child labor, dangerous working environments and other inhumane conditions are examples of issues being brought into the open. All companies and organizations aiming at long-term profitability and credibility are starting to realize that they must act in accordance with norms of right and wrong."[8]

The costs of an organization go beyond its doors. There are often costs to society that linger far longer than the life of a corporation. Hazardous waste sites such as those targeted by the U.S. Environmental Protection Agency (EPA) Superfund programs are among the more obvious, but these costs can appear while the organization is in operation as well.

To see this, think about the quality costs (or poor quality costs) previously discussed. These are usually quantified in terms of scrap and rework, warranty, or other tangible costs. As we saw, however, these constitute only the tip of the iceberg (Figure 1.2).

What about the hidden costs or long-term losses related to engineering/management time, inventory, customer dissatisfaction, and lost market share? Can we quantify these? Perhaps, but not accurately. Indeed, we must find a way to approximate these hidden and long-term losses, because they're the largest contributors to total quality loss. Taguchi Methods uses the Quality Loss Function (QLF) for this purpose.

The way in which the QLF is established depends on the type of quality characteristic involved. A quality characteristic is whatever we measure to judge performance (quality). There are five types of quality characteristics:

1. Nominal-the-best (achieving a desired target value with minimal variation; for example, dimension and output voltage)

2. Smaller-the-better (minimizing a response; for example, shrinkage and wear)

3. Larger-the-better (maximizing a response; for example, pull-off force and tensile strength)

4. Attribute (classifying and/or counting data; for example, appearance)

5. Dynamic (response varies depending on input; for example, speed of a fan drive should vary depending on the engine temperature)

The QLF will not be demonstrated for a nominal-the-best quality characteristic. From an engineering standpoint, the losses of concern are those caused when a product's quality characteristic deviates from its desired target value. For example, consider an AC/DC converting circuit where the AC input is 110 volts and the circuit is to output 115 DC volts. The output voltage is the quality characteristic of interest, and its desired target value is 115 volts. Any deviation from 115 volts is considered functional variation and will cause some loss.

Suppose there are four factories producing these circuits under the same specifications, $115 + 3$ volts, and their output is as shown in Figure 1.7. Suppose further that all four factories carry out 100% inspection (let's even naively assume it is 100% effective), so that only those pieces within specifications are shipped out. If you're the consumer and wish to buy the circuits from one of the four factories, which would you choose (assuming that the price is the same)?

Although all four factories are shipping out circuits that meet the engineering specifications, Factory No. 4 appears to offer a more uniform product (that is, the variation around the 115-volt target is less at this factory than at the three other factories).

In this way of thinking, loss occurs not only when a product is outside the specifications, but also when a product falls within the specifications. Further, it's reasonable to believe that loss continually increases as a product deviates further from the target value, as the parabola (QLF) in Figure 1.8 illustrates. Although a loss function may take on many forms, Taguchi has found that the simple quadratic function approximates the behavior of loss in many instances.

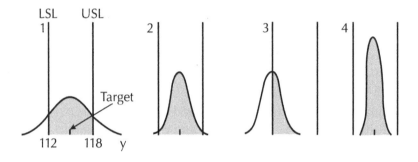

Figure 1.7   Output distribution from four factories.

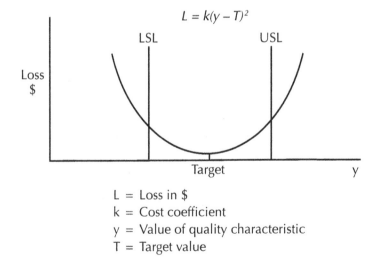

Figure 1.8   The quality loss function.

Since the QLF curve is quadratic in nature, loss increases by the square of the distance from the target value. Thus, if a deviation of 0.02mm from the target value generates a 20 cents loss, then a deviation of 0.04mm would cost 80 cents, a deviation of 0.06mm would cost $1.80, and so forth. In other words, if deviation is doubled, the loss is quadrupled. If it's tripled, the loss increases nine times. For smaller the-better quality characteristics such as part shrinkage, or larger the-better quality characteristics such as tensile strength, the QLF may become a half parabola. In any event, belief in the QLF promotes efforts to continually reduce the variation in a product's quality characteristics. Taguchi's quality engineering methodology is a vehicle for attaining such improvements. Of course, the formula is adjusted to match each particular situation because the cost-to-distance-from-mean relationship will vary.

The QLF was used to estimate the average quality loss from each of the four factories, as illustrated in Figure 1.9. Notice that the smallest average quality loss was obtained from Factory No. 4, the factory with the highest quality. In short, the QLF is a measure of quality in monetary units that reflects not only immediate costs, such as scrap and rework, but long-term losses as well.

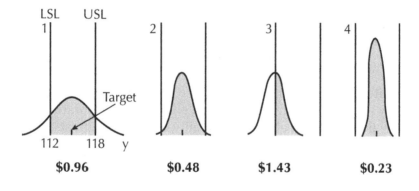

Figure 1.9 Average quality loss per piece.

QUALITY/ACCOUNTING INTERFACE

Some companies believe that implementing a quality cost program would require extensive accounting system changes and additional staff. Others believe that their present cost accounting system is sufficient to identify all areas requiring management attention. Unfortunately, accounting systems were not designed to demonstrate the impact of the quality of performance (thought to be subjective measurement) on overall operating costs. That is why many of these costs have remained hidden.

The identification and collection of quality costs must be comprehensive if the system is to be effective, but it also must be practical. The collection and reporting of quality costs should be designed in conjunction with the basic company cost accounting system (see Appendix A, Basic Financial Concepts). If large elements of quality costs are incurred but not accurately identified within the cost accounting system (for example, scrap, rework, or redesign costs), estimates should be used until the system can be adjusted. This will be necessary before a reasonable picture of total quality costs can be portrayed as a justification for improvement. Also, if these quality-related elements are to become a prime target for cost reduction, they cannot be buried somewhere within other accounts. They must be clearly visible.

For all of the cited reasons, it is essential that both the in-house descriptions and the responsibility for quality cost collection, compilation, and reporting be a function of the controller's office—as a service to the quality management function. A controller's procedure for quality costs is necessary to provide company definitions or estimating technique, and location of elements within the company manual of accounts (that is, all that is needed to accurately portray total cost to the company). Holding the controller responsible for quality cost measurement will establish standards for the quality cost program:

- It will provide the stamp of financial validity.

- It will assure that collection costs remain within practical limits.

- It will provide an opportunity for the development of effective teamwork between the controller and the quality function, with both organizations seeking cost benefits for the company.

In reality, it is reasonable to expect that the controller will not be eager to have an already overworked staff address an additional system for tracking costs. Therefore, the practical value of the quality cost system must be "sold" to the decision makers (see Chapter 3, Quality Cost Program Implementation).

Nevertheless, an internal quality cost procedure will serve to direct the acquisition of specific quality cost data needed to support the company's quality improvement strategies and goals.

In developing the details of a quality cost system, there are two important criteria by which to be guided: (1) know that quality costs are a tool to justify improvement actions and measure their effectiveness; and (2) know that costs from insignificant activities hurt the effective use of quality costs.

If all significant quality costs are captured and utilized, the objectives of the quality/accounting interface—quality cost improvement—can be justified and accomplished. Consistency and integrity will pay off.

For many industries, the measurement of quality costs is a competitive advantage and most firms are unwilling to share this information. Many publicly held firms feel that shareholders should not be told the costs of failure. This makes benchmarking a difficult proposition. Also, since there is not a widespread standard for what to include and what to leave out of a quality cost measure, direct comparisons from firm to firm are not reliable. Comparisons with others are meaningless. Comparison with your own past performance is what really matters. Incremental improvements in quality costs are what counts.

MANAGEMENT OF QUALITY COSTS

Managing quality costs begins with a general understanding and belief that improving quality performance, as related to product or service, and improving quality costs are synonymous (the economics of quality). The next step is to recognize that measurable quality improvement can also have a tangible effect on other business measures such as sales and market share. The proviso, however, is that quality costs must be measured and must reflect cost or lost opportunities to the company.

It should be further understood that the cost-of-quality analysis is a comprehensive system, not a piecemeal tool. Many Six Sigma practitioners suggest that cost-of-quality analysis (often referred to as merely "cost of poor quality") is only a minor tool used as part of their improvement methodology. This can be done, but it misses the point. All improvement methodologies need guidance. Determining what project is first and where to go next is an executive decision that must be guided by understanding what promises the best benefit. Cost of quality analysis is how that guidance is informed, by looking at prevention, appraisal, and failure costs systematically. For other business demands beyond process improvement methodologies, some organizations use an ad hoc method of attacking issues piecemeal. There is a danger in responding to a customer problem only with added internal operations, such as inspections or tests. For service operations, this could mean more operators. While this may solve the immediate customer problem, its added costs may, in fact, destroy the profit potential. A comprehensive quality management program will force the analysis of all associated quality costs, making these added internal costs appear to clearly adjust one step toward the ultimate resolution—prevention of the root cause of the problem.

By now it should be obvious that a quality cost system has the potential to be a valuable tool in the overall management of a business. It can indicate the health of management performance in many areas of a company. It will measure the cost of error-related activities in these areas. A quality cost program should, therefore, become an integral part of any quality improvement activity. Overall quality cost numbers will point out the potential for improvement and they will provide management with the basis for measuring the improvement accomplished.

In addition to being an overall indicator of quality effectiveness, quality cost numbers are an important asset in the establishment of priorities for needed corrective action. Some companies continue to live with less-than-perfect performance levels because they believe it would be more expensive to improve. Perhaps the greatest contribution of quality cost systems in this aspect of a business is showing the payoff potential for corrective actions and justifying their accomplishment. For example, the real profitability of investment in an expensive new tool, machine, or computer system may be obscured by incomplete data about the costs of inspection, sorting, rework, repair, scrap, and the risk that nonconforming product, service, or information will reach the customer. Profitable firms may be lured into applying a technological fix to an issue better fixed by focus on the mundane.

The central part of managing quality costs is reducing failure costs. For example, failure costs could be organized in Pareto fashion for elimination (the vital few as opposed to the trivial many), starting with the highest cost items. If a company's basic quality measurement system cannot identify defects or problems to which quality costs can be attached, the first corrective action required is to establish a system that can. Failure costs cannot be progressively reduced without a parallel system to assist in tracking down the defect causes for elimination. At best, without a defect or problem reporting system, only the most obvious problems, the so-called "fires," can be pursued. The not-so-obvious problems will remain hidden in the accepted cost of doing business. Identification and resolution of these otherwise hidden problems is the first major payoff of a quality cost program.

The next step in managing quality costs is to analyze the need for current appraisal costs. Are we taking too high a risk of excessive failure costs by not having a sufficient appraisal program? Or are we spending too much for appraisal, especially considering the improved levels of performance we have achieved? Quality cost analyses, in conjunction with risk analysis, have been used to set desired levels of appraisal activity. In a more constructive way, quality cost analyses also have been used to validate that appraisal activities are not a substitute for adequate prevention activities.

Like failure and appraisal costs, prevention costs of quality are managed through careful analysis leading to improvement actions. Prevention costs are an investment in the discovery, incorporation, and maintenance of defect prevention disciplines for all operations affecting the quality of product or service. Prevention efforts must be applied in a targeted fashion, not evenly across the board. Much improvement has been demonstrated through reallocation of prevention effort from areas having little effect to areas where it really pays off. Mapping failure costs, appraisal costs, and prevention costs according to organization process flows can help answer the question about whether resources are properly deployed.

If not introduced in a positive manner, a quality cost program that exposes waste, error, and unnecessary expenditures can have negative repercussions, even in a profitable company well managed for quality. For this reason, it is essential that all affected employees, starting with management, be carefully informed and understand that quality cost analysis is a tool for improving the economics of operation. It doesn't matter what the starting numbers are. Variations in the application of quality costs—in the business itself, in accounting systems, and in overall performance—make each company unique, so comparisons with other companies are meaningless and must be avoided. The most important number, the very essence of quality cost objectives, is the amount of measurable improvement from year to year.

If the quality cost program is kept simple and practical, it will support the initiative to improve quality in all operations—the initiative of a quality-driven or excellence-driven management system. When a quality cost program is launched, it should be carefully planned to reach the desired objectives. A quality cost program need not identify all elements of quality costs (as described in Appendix B, Detailed Description of Quality Cost Elements); rather, it should concentrate on the quality cost elements most significantly affecting your company.

Judgment as to what is most significant should be based on more than magnitude. It has been found that small expenses generated for some elements can be just as significant as huge expenses for other elements. The direct cost of various wastes may not reflect equally in the eyes of customers. In any event, the program must include all major quality cost elements, even if some will ultimately be estimated. After the initial study, the program can be reevaluated and refined with additional details as necessary. For most companies, this initial approach will delineate many improvement opportunities. Managing quality costs means acting on opportunities and reaping financial and reputational rewards, as well as quality improvements contained therein.

Total quality costs are intended to represent the difference between the actual cost of a product or service and what the cost would be if quality were perfect. It is, as previously ascribed to Juran, "gold in the mine" just waiting to be extracted. When you zero in on the elimination of failure costs and then challenge the level of appraisal costs, you will not only be managing the cost of quality, you will be mining gold.

ISO 9000 SERIES OF STANDARDS AND QUALITY COSTS

ISO 9000

Since 1987, businesses of all types have chosen to become certified to the quality system standard known as ISO 9000, which is published by the International Organization for Standardization. The standard has evolved since its inception. In 1999, these standards were known as ISO 9000–9004. ISO 9001 was based on 20 elements and used as a checklist. In 2000, ISO 9001 changed again to reflect the process approach and five major clauses aimed at helping organizations define their major processes, focus on performance, and eliminate the checklist mentality.

The revised 9001 includes a number of new clauses that can be used to reduce quality costs; discussion that follows will look at key clauses that may be used to control the cost of poor quality and reduce costs. Inputs from ISO 9004:2009 are also included in the discussion of the various clauses of ISO 9001:2008.

The ISO 9001 standard defines and specifies the elements of a quality system. The quality system can be viewed as the organizational structure, the documented procedures and resources that an organization employs to manage quality. The ISO 9001 standard recommends that the effectiveness of the quality system be measured. Although there are many measures possible, ranging from counting defects to implementing sophisticated customer satisfaction surveys, the measures of most general interest are likely to be financial. Money is the universal language of business and is at least a consideration in most other enterprises.

Our approach will be to step through the clauses in the standard and identify the category of quality cost that might be found in that clause. We will use the previously defined PAF model for cost categorization: Prevention–Appraisal–Failure costs.

Relevant ISO Documents

ISO 9001, Clause 4: Quality Management System

These introductory elements of the standard define the basic structure of an effective quality management system. First there is the requirement to define all processes, their applications and interactions. Then there are requirements to maintain a quality manual and define structures to control documents and records. These clauses do not have a direct effect on cost of quality (COQ), but ineffective application will increase organizational costs, especially the cost of conformance.

ISO 9001, Clause 5: Management Responsibility

ISO 9001, Clauses 5.1–5.4 have a soft effect on cost. The key requirements defined are to have a quality policy and quality objectives and to perform management reviews. The objectives must be measurable and consistent with the quality policy. Measurable objectives are needed to determine whether the objectives have been met.

ISO 9001, Clause 5.2 defines a commitment to improve customer satisfaction by meeting customer requirements. Examples of customer satisfaction requirements are:

- On-time deliveries
- Reduction of order backlogs, nonconforming material, scrap, and inventory

ISO 9001, Clause 5.6 is the most important part of Clause 5, the definition of reviews conducted by top management. The reviews provide opportunities to improve the QMS, the quality policy, and the quality objectives. The inputs include audit results, customer feedback, process performance and product conformity, the status of corrective and preventive actions, and recommendations for improvement. The outputs are decisions and actions to improve QMS effectiveness by improving its processes with respect to customer needs.

The management review inputs and responses provide data that can be used in determining the cost of poor quality and the reduction over time of these costs that can be called the value of quality improvement. These may be prevention or appraisal costs in the P A F model of quality costs.

ISO 9001, Clause 6: Managing Resources

The lack of customer satisfaction is one measure of the cost of poor quality. The elements of Clause 6 require resources for the implementation and improvement of the QMS and enhancement of customer satisfaction. Worker incompetence is one cause of poor quality. This can be improved by increasing the education level, training, skills, and experience of the organization's personnel. The cost of this improvement would be prevention cost.

Infrastructure and work environment are two important aspects of resource availability. Problems in either area can have a negative effect on the quality of products and services.

The organization's resources (such as equipment, facilities, materials, energy, knowledge, finance, and people) must be managed to ensure their availability for future activities.

ISO 9004:2009, Clause 6.2 Financial Resources, addresses processes that should be established for monitoring, controlling, and reporting the effective allocation and efficient usage of financial resources related to the organization's objectives. Reporting can provide means for determining ineffective or inefficient activities and initiating suitable improvement actions. Such actions should be included in management reviews that can positively influence the financial results of the organization.

Improving the effectiveness and efficiency of the management system can positively influence the financial results of the organization in many ways:

- Internally, by reducing process and product failures and eliminating the waste of materials or time

- Externally, by reducing product failures, costs of compensation under guarantees and warranties, product liabilities and other legal exposure, costs of lost customers and markets

ISO 9004:2009, Clause 6.4 Suppliers and Partners, says that the organization should establish and maintain processes to identify, select, and evaluate its suppliers and partners in order to improve their capabilities and to ensure that the products and other resources they provide meet the needs and expectations of the organization. Together with its suppliers and partners, the organization should continually improve the quality, price and delivery of products provided by suppliers and partners and the effectiveness of their management systems. Costs associated with these activities are most commonly classified as prevention costs.

ISO 9001, Clause 7: Product Realization

Clause 7 contains a number of requirements that are considered "soft" in nature because of the difficulty associated with measuring their cost. However, if problems occur, there will be associated costs.

Clause 7.1, "planning of product realization," covers planning of the production processes that include product requirements, manufacturing processes, documentation, resources needed, acceptance criteria and verification, validation, monitoring and inspection activities, and records.

Clause 7.2, "customer-related processes," contains customer-specified product requirements including delivery and post-delivery activities. It also includes review of statutory and regulatory requirements and customer communication. Clause 7.2.2 adds a review of requirements related to the product such as contract or order requirements. Finally, Clause 7.2.3 adds implementation of effective arrangements for communicating with the customer on product information, enquiries, contracts, and customer complaints.

Clause 7.3 covers design and development process including planning, inputs, outputs, design review, design verification, validation, and design and development changes. The organization must manage the interfaces between various groups.

Clause 7.4 outlines the purchasing process including criteria for choosing and evaluating suppliers, providing purchasing information, and verification of purchased products.

Clause 7.5 contains a description of production and service provision, identification, and traceability. This clause also includes requirements for the care of customer property and product preservation. Clause 7.5.2 describes validation of production and service provision processes.

Clause 7.6 covers control of monitoring and measurement to insure conformity of the product to its requirements. To insure valid results, monitoring and measurement equipment is calibrated and re-adjusted where necessary, safeguarded from adjustments that would invalidate the measurement results, and protected from damage and deterioration. The organization must maintain the results of calibration and verification.

All of these ISO 9001, Clause 7 expenses may be either prevention or appraisal costs, depending on the work processes used by the organization.

ISO 9001, Clause 8: Measurement, Analysis and Improvement

Clause 8 contains measurable requirements that can be used to directly determine the cost of poor quality. This clause contains activities to measure, monitor, and improve the quality management system.

Clause 8.1 contains requirements for planning and implementing monitoring, measurement, analysis, and improvement of the QMS. The goals are to demonstrate conformity to product requirements, ensure conformity of the QMS, and continually improve its effectiveness. Of course, when the demonstrations fall short of the targets, the cost of poor quality (or failure cost) can be measured.

Clause 8.2 and 8.3 require process and product monitoring and measurement of QMS performance, including customer satisfaction, internal audit, and control of nonconforming product. These data are useful in determining quality costs.

In Clause 8.2.1, the measurement of customer perception of how well their requirements are met, provides valuable insight into the quality level provided. Of course, the internal audit (Clause 8.2.2) is a source of information on the QMS quality levels and corrective actions taken. Perhaps the best sources of data and quality level information are Clauses 8.2.3 and 8.2.4, addressing monitoring and measurement of processes and product. Quality costs lie in rework, testing, warranties, inspections, services, damaged reputations, and litigation after delivery of poor quality products or services. These are normally included in the appraisal cost category.

Clause 8.4, addressing data analysis, is used to reveal actionable information about customer satisfaction, product conformity to requirements, product and process trends and characteristics, preventive action opportunities, and supplier measurements. These data may be used to demonstrate the suitability and effectiveness of the quality management system and to evaluate the opportunities for improvement of the system. The goals are to provide information relating to customer satisfaction, conformity to product requirements, opportunities for preventive action, and supplier quality. Failure costs lie in rework, testing, inspections, services, warrantees damaged reputation, and litigation that results from doing the wrong thing.

The improvement Clause 8.5 includes corrective and preventive actions, which provide the best measurements of cost of poor quality. Clause 8.5.3 describes the preventive action process and includes identifying potential nonconformities, evaluating the need for preventive action, implementing and reviewing results, and keeping records of actions and results. The corrective action process (Clause 8.5.2) describes methods to stop the recurrence of nonconformities and drive improvement. Corrective actions are initiated by customer complaints, late deliveries, product nonconformities, and so on and are usually classified as failure costs. This allows visibility of the balance between preventive actions and corrective actions.

Summary of the Cost of Poor Quality Opportunities from the Use of ISO 9001:2008 and ISO 9004:2009

Compliance to ISO 9001:2008 provides many opportunities for determining the COQ. Some of the information is soft and it is necessary to estimate costs. One example is a poor level of customer satisfaction. The cost to a company can only be estimated. However, if the market is reduced because of poor customer satisfaction, actual data can be obtained to estimate the cost. Organizations may choose to calculate this cost (or lost revenue), but care must be taken to count only clear cases of lost sales tied to quality issues.

Clause 8 provides the best sources for estimating COQ. Clauses 8.4 (data analysis) and 8.5 (preventive and corrective action) provide measurements that can be used. Also, management review in Clause 5 provides an excellent source of data because it contains summaries of the results of other clauses.

Quality costs can be greatly reduced when an organization correctly implements the following tools of 9001: quality policy, measurable quality objectives, audit results, data analysis, corrective and preventive action, and management review.

Note that there are other standards that provide data when properly implemented. ISO 10014 and TL 9000 are two standards that when properly implemented can provide COQ data.

ISO 10014:2006 Quality Management—Guidelines for Realizing Financial and Economic Benefits

This standard contains guidelines for realizing financial and economic benefits through adoption by top management of the eight management principles:

1. Customer focus

2. Leadership

3. Involvement of people

4. Process approach

5. System approach to management

6. Continual improvement

7. Factual approach to decision making

8. Mutual beneficial supplier relationships

Application of ISO 10014 can result in numerous financial benefits that can be measured and applied to improved quality costs. These include improvements in profitability, costs, return on investments, customer retention and loyalty, use of available resources, supply chain performance, and time to market.

ISO 10014 uses the plan, do, check, act (PDCA) approach to describe the "factual approach to decision making" and "mutually beneficial supplier relationships." The achievable benefits of each can be applied to the principles of quality cost.

The TL 9000 Standard

TL 9000 contains two types of quality management procedures for the telecommunication industry: quality requirements and measurements. The requirements are based on ISO 9001 and consist of 92 added requirements (adders), most of which can have a positive effect on COQ. Adders are classified according to the following categories:

• Common adders

• Hardware adders

- Software adders
- Service adders
- Hardware and service adders
- Hardware and software adders

Effect of Adders on Cost of Quality

There are 92 adders currently included in TL 9000, Release 5. The key adders for each of the sections of ISO 9001 are described here.

Clauses 5.1–5.4 include six adders that have a soft effect on costs. Two adders affect requirements in Clause 6. These are:

- 5.2.C.1, Customer Relationship Development
- 5.2.C.2, Customer Communications Methods

Clause 6, Managing Resources, addresses resources needed to implement and improve the QMS and enhance customer satisfaction. To satisfy 5.2.C.1 and 5.2.C.2 will require expenditure of additional resources. Clause 6 includes nine adders that are soft in nature.

Clause 7 is a large clause with 60 adders. Sub-clause 7.1 includes six adders, three of which will greatly affect the COQ. These are:

- 7.1.C.1, Life Cycle Model
- 7.1.C.2, Disaster Recovery
- 7.1.C.3, End of Life Planning

Sub-clause 7.2 contains eight adders, four of which will affect the COQ measurement. These are:

- 7.2.3.C.2, Problem Severity Classification
- 7.2.3.C.3, Problem Escalation
- 7.2.3.HS.1, Product Replacement
- 7.2.3.HS.2, Design and Development Process Measurements

Sub-clause 7.3 includes 26 adders. It contains a new adder, 7.3.1.C.4, Risk Management Plan, which has the goal of controlling risks that can impact cost, schedule, and product quality or performance. Other adders that may affect the COQ are:

- 7.3.1.C.1, Project Plan
- 7.3.1.C.3, Test Planning
- 7.3.1.C.4, Risk Management Plan
- 7.3.1.HS.2, Design and Development Process Quality Measurement Planning and Implementation

- 7.3.2.C.1, Customer and Supplier Input
- 7.3.5HS.1, Stress Testing
- 7.3.5.HS.2, Abnormal Conditions
- 7.3.7.C.1, Change Management Process
- 7.3.7.C.2, Informing Customers
- 7.3.7.C.3, Problem Resolution
- 7.3.7.H.1, Component Changes

Sub-clause 7.4 includes one adder that affects COQ:

- 7.4.1.C.2, Supplier Performance Measurement

Sub-clause 7.5 contains 17 adders. The following can have an effect on COQ:

- 7.5.1.C.1, Service Resources
- 7.5.1.HS.1, Emergency Service
- 7.5.1.HV.1, Operational Changes
- 7.5.3.H.1, Traceability for Recall
- 7.5.5.HV.1, Deterioration

Clause adders are most likely to affect the COQ because these address where the data related to quality measurements are found. There are 15 adders relating to Clause 8.

Sub-clause 8.2 has nine adders associated with it, some of which contain data that can be applied to COQ.

- 8.2.1.C.1, Customer Satisfaction Data
- 8.2.3.C.1, Process Measurement
- 8.2.4.H.4, Testing of Repair and Return Products
- 8.2.4.HV.2, Inspection and Test Records

Sub-clause 8.4 has three adders associated with it.

- 8.4.C.1, Trend Analysis of Nonconforming Product
- 8.4.HS.1, Field Performance Data
- 8.4.V.1, Service Performance Data

Sub-clause 8.5 has two adders associated with it.

- 8.5.1.C.1, Continual Improvement Programs
- 8.5.2.S.1, Problem Resolution

Using TL 9000 Adders to Estimate the Cost of Quality

First, let us look at the effect adders can have on COQ. Most of the adders are soft in nature and the effect on COQ will depend on the accuracy of the estimation process. The adders from Clauses 5 and 6 will have a soft effect on COQ. The cost will then be a judgment based on the history of the adders. Clauses 7 and 8 contain adders that can provide substantial data for COQ estimates.

In Sub-clause 7.1, Planning of the Life Cycle Model (7.1.C.1), Disaster Recovery (7.1.C.2), and End of Life Planning (7.1.C.3) will result in measurable costs that affect the COQ. This is also true in the following adders defined in Clauses 7.2 and 7.3:

- 7.2.3.C.3, Problem Escalation
- 7.2.3.HS.1, Product Replacement
- 7.3.1.C.4, Risk Management Plan
- 7.3.5.HS.2, Abnormal Conditions
- 7.3.7.C.1, Change Management Process
- 7.3.7.C.3, Problem Resolution
- 7.3.7.H.1, Component Changes
- 7.5.1.HS.1, Emergency Service
- 7.5.1.HV.1, Operational Changes
- 7.5.3.H.1, Traceability for Recall
- 7.5.5.HV.1, Deterioration

The adders in Clause 8 will mainly provide data that can be used in COQ calculations. The adders most likely to provide COQ data are listed here.

- 8.2.1.C.1, Customer Satisfaction Data
- 8.2.3.C.1, Process Measurement
- 8.2.4.H.4, Testing of Repair and Return Products
- 8.2.4.HV.2, Inspection and Test Records
- 8.4.C.1, Trend Analysis of Nonconforming Product
- 8.4.HS.1, Field Performance Data
- 8.4.V.1, Service Performance Data
- 8.5.1.C.1, Continual Improvement Programs
- 8.5.2.S.1, Problem Resolution

The value of these adders in a COQ program will depend on the accuracy of the data gathered to support compliance.

The TL 9000 Measurements Program

The measurements program provides a means for customer comparison of competing company results. These data can be used in benchmarking the top quality organizations and have resulted in quality improvements throughout the industry. All TL certified organizations must submit their product/ services data on a regular basis. The latest version of the measurements handbook (Release 4.5) was published July 2010.

This program defines requirements for measurements reporting including conformance to measurements profile; applicable product categories; customer source data; acceptable alternative measurements; report frequency and method; use of fiscal periods and calendar days; reporting of compared and research data; product exclusions; measurement applicability; calculation of normalization units; format of report data; and the benefits of using TL 9000 measurement data.

Common Measurements details specific requirements for measuring and reporting TL 9000 measurements that apply to all product categories. These include the number of problems reported to the organization by customers (NPR), the performance of the organization in fixing problems (FRT and OFR), and the ability of the organization to deliver its products and services when the customer wants them (OTD).

Outage Measurements define outages and how to measure them, including systems outages (SO), network elements outages (NEO), and support service-caused outages (SSO). The outages are measured in events and normalized duration for both organization-responsible and customer-responsible events. Field Returns measures the amount of product returned to organizations by customers over three shipping periods: early period (ERI), one year (YRR), and long term (LTR). This also measures the normalized one-year return rate (NYR).

There are two software measurements. Software Fix Quality (SFQ) measures the quality of software fixes delivered to the field, and Software Problem Reports (SPR) provides a subset of problem reports (see NPR) that apply to software only.

Service Quality (SQ) is a measure of conformance of a service to a specified criterion.

Product category tables define the approximately 130 product categories to be used in classifying products and reporting data so that the measurement of like product can be normalized and compared.

TL 9000 Customer Satisfaction Measurements Guidelines offers guidance in measuring customer satisfaction. These measurements are not reported to the Measurements Repository.

Using TL 9000 Measurements to Estimate the Cost of Quality

Common measurements apply to all products. The first is the number of problem reports (NPR). The purpose of this measurement is to evaluate the number of problems or complaints during field operations in order to reduce associated costs and revenue losses. Both customers and suppliers provide data for NPR measurements. This will induce joint efforts by the organization and its customers and suppliers to reduce costs by improving quality. Typical target audiences for NPR measurements are customer maintenance, engineering, technical support, supplier technical support, manufacturing management, and engineering management.

Fix response time (FRT) represents the responsiveness of the organization to a subset of customer-reported problems that require a change to the product. Overdue fix responsiveness (OFR) measures the rate of closure of overdue hardware and software problems and all service problems.

FRT measures the responsiveness to problem reports that may require changes to the product's hardware, documentation, procedures, and software. The FRT measurement for each product category includes the following:

- Percent hardware/software major problems fixed within 30 days and minor problems fixed within 180 days

- Percent service problems fixed on time

OFR costs may come from lost future orders, missed contract obligations, product procedure changes, and costs due to increased personnel efforts. On-time delivery (OTD) measures the improvement of the organization after fixes have been applied. OTD consists of installed order fulfillment, orderable line item order fulfillment, and service order fulfillment.

System Outage Measurements

The system outage measurement is used to evaluate the hardware and software downtime performance and outage frequency during field operations in order to reduce costs and revenue impacts. An outage is a measure of complete loss of all or part of a system. There are four categories of outages measurements:

- Annualized outage frequency

- Annualized downtime

- Annualized supplier attributable outage frequency

- Annualized supplier attributable downtime

Hardware-only Measurement

Return rate applies to field-replaceable hardware products such as circuit packs but not to cable, optical fiber, or mechanical circuit packs. The purposes of return rate measurement are to determine the quality of products initially received by customers, to determine areas that need corrective action, and to help determine life-cycle costs. Return rates are computed for initial return rate (IRR), one-year return rate (YRR), and long-term return rate (LTR).

Software Measurements

There are three software measurement options: (1) software release application and patching, (2) software updates, and (3) software update and patching. Table 1 summarizes the measurements that apply to each of the options.

Table 1.1 Summary of measurement options.

Measurement Option	Applications
Software release application and patching	Applies to software used for installation and maintenance
Software updates	Applies to products that use software updates for both installation and maintenance
Software update and patching	Applies to software used for installation, software updates, and patches for maintenance

Service Measurement

Service quality metrics provide quality measurement information for evaluation and continuous improvement of the service being measured. Service quality includes the following measurements:

- Percent conforming installation audits
- Percent successful maintenance visits without callbacks
- Percent successful repairs
- Percent conforming call center calls resolved within agreed-upon time
- Percent support service transactions without a defect.

Summary of ISO 9000 Family Contributions to Measuring Cost of Quality

In the requirements document, Clause 8.4 is used to analyze product stored in its database. This analysis is used to evaluate improvement of the quality management system. It uses data generated as a result of monitoring and measurement and other relevant sources and after analysis produces information relating to customer satisfaction, conformity to requirements, characteristics and trends of processes and products, opportunities for preventive action, and data on suppliers.

Clause 8.5 can be used to provide information on corrective and preventive actions. This includes results of actions taken and a review of the effectiveness of these actions. Other information gathered as result of Clauses 7 and 8 provide further information on COQ and its improvement.

TL 9000 provides a tremendous opportunity to measure and improve COQ at telecommunications organizations. This is due to the added requirements that expand the data gathering capability of ISO 9001. TL 9000 also has measurement requirements that further expand the quality improvement capabilities and the ability to measure COQ.

ISO/TS 16949 and Quality Costs—The Automotive Industry

The 2009 version of the International Organization for Standardization's (ISO) Technical Standard (TS) for the global automotive industry is called "Quality management systems—Particular requirements for the application of ISO 9001:2008 for automotive production and relevant service part organizations." This Technical Standard is an out growth of the U.S. Automotive Industries' Quality System Requirements (QS) 9000 system that was in effect from 1994 through 2002.

This TS, as well as other industry specific applications of ISO 9001, uses the ISO 9001 standard verbatim and then adds industry specific information. ISO 9001 does not call out anything related to the principles of Quality Costs. ISO/TS 16949 does by using the term 'Cost of Poor Quality.'

In paragraph 5.6.1.1 Quality Management System Performance, the TS specifically states: "Part of the management review shall be the monitoring of quality objectives, and the regular reporting and evaluation of the cost of poor quality (see 8.4.1 and 8.5.1)." This paragraph continues the Cost of Poor Quality requirement by stating: "These results shall be recorded to provide, as a minimum, evidence of the achievement of: the quality objectives specified in the business plan, and customer satisfaction with product supplied."

The note to see paragraphs 8.4.1 (Analysis and Use of Data) and 8.5.1 (Continual Improvement) are the standard text of ISO 9001 and require looking at data trends and improving the effectiveness of the quality management system.

Another note about ISO/TS 16949:2009 is around the use of the term "Cost" versus "Quality Cost." In analyzing the Quality Cost of a product, the international automotive community also wants their suppliers to be very conscious of general costs and call out specific examples in paragraphs 7.3.2.1 (Product Design Input), 7.3.2.2 (Manufacturing Process Design Input) and in 7.3.4.1 (Monitoring) were cost is treated as things associated with reliability, durability, productivity, process capability, quality risks or lead times. An argument could be put forward that these costs are part of the internal failure category of Quality Costs. Because of this, it can be expected that the standard intends to look at prevention and appraisal costs, not just failure costs, or "cost of poor execution."

End Notes

1. Chartered Institute of Management Accountants survey "Management Accounting Tools for Today and Tomorrow" July 2009.

2. Sower, Victor E., and Ross Quarles; "Cost of Quality Usage and Its Relationship to Quality Systems Maturity"; Working Paper series—Center for Business and Economic Development at Sam Houston State University; November, 2002; pp. 10–12.

3. The National Conference for Quality, *Quality Progress* 15, no. 5 (May 1952): 14–17.

4. H. J. Harrington, *Poor-Quality Cost* (Milwaukee: ASQC Quality Press, 1987).

5. Juran, J. M., A. Blanton Godfrey, and Frank M. Gryna, "Section 8 Quality and Costs" in *Juran's Quality Handbook,* 5th edition (New York: McGraw-Hill, 1999).

6. Brown, F. X. and R. W. Kane, "Quality Costs and Profit Performance" in *Annual Technical Conference Transactions* (Milwaukee: American Society for Quality Control, 1975).

7. Material for this section was extracted from publications of the American Supplier Institute (ASI), Dearborn, MI: Diane M. Byrne and Nancy E. Ryan, eds., *Taguchi Methods and QFD.* (Dearborn, MI: ASI Press, 1988); William E. Eureka and Nancy E. Ryan, eds., *The Customer-Driven Company* (Dearborn, MI: ASI Press, 1988); Lance A. Ealey, *Quality by Design,* (Dearborn, MI: ASI Press, 1988).

8. Quoted from ASQ website: www.asq.org/social-responsibility/about/what-is-it.html

Chapter 2

Quality Cost System Definitions

Almost every department of a company spends money on labor or materials that have specific impact on the quality of product or service provided to customers. It's probably impossible to account for all of these costs, but attempts to do so have led to many different descriptions offered for the cost of quality. This chapter attempts to glean from these many efforts those elements of quality costs that have proven useful on a broad scale.

We start with a general description of quality cost categories. Next, we will build more depth by a detailed description of quality cost elements (see Appendix B, "Detailed Description of Quality Cost Elements"). These can be applied, as applicable and practical, to the development of an individual cost-of-quality program.

QUALITY COST CATEGORIES

As discussed in Chapter 1, quality costs have been categorized as prevention, appraisal, and failure costs. Failure costs are farther divided into internal and external failure costs.

Prevention costs are associated with all activities specifically designed to prevent poor quality in products or services. Examples include the costs of new product review, quality planning, supplier capability surveys, process capability evaluations, quality improvement team meetings, quality improvement projects, design for Six Sigma, kaizen teams, cellular layout activities, gauging studies, SPC (X & R), poka-yoke (error proofing) devices, quality education, and quality training.

A warning is needed here: prevention costs could be misinterpreted in two ways.

First, application of the definition of prevention costs could be unclear. Extra appraisal and failure costs may be incurred to *prevent* more expensive failure costs (for example, added inspections and rework to prevent newly found defects from reaching the customer). These clearly are not prevention costs. But in the same sense, costs incurred to solve problems (corrective action or failure analysis costs) can be viewed as either part of the problem cost (failure cost) or the cost incurred to prevent the problem in the future (prevention cost). In this case, it doesn't really matter in which category the costs are accumulated as long as there is consistency. This consistency will be developed as you plan and create an individualized cost-of-quality measure. The detailed descriptions in Appendix B will attempt to identify elements that might be viewed this way.

The second way in which prevention costs could be misunderstood occurs whenever an individual is engaged in prevention activities as an integral but small part of a regular job assignment. This may be a highly significant activity, such as control charting by the production operator, in which case part of the operator's cost could be considered prevention in the quality cost report. However, some consider this type of prevention activity a desirable built-in self-discipline cost that is part of normal operating expense. This may also include allocations for automated mechanisms such as a self-checking machine tool, automatic process control equipment, or a software-based inspection edit for service processing. On the other hand, individuals such as engineers or analysts may work full-time for short periods in activities (such as quality improvement projects) designed specifically to prevent defects or solve other quality problems further along in the process. This type of activity is clearly intended to be a part of prevention costs, the objective of the activity being to create a system that avoids process flaws. Care should be taken to not include activities where avoidance never happens.

Appraisal costs are costs associated with measuring, evaluating, or auditing products or services to assure conformance to quality standards and performance requirements. These include the costs of incoming and source inspection/test of purchased material; validation, verification, and checking activities; in-process and final inspection/test; product, process, or service audits; required compliance system costs (such as those needed for ISO, AS, TS, HACCP, ITAR); calibration of measuring and test equipment; and the costs of associated supplies and materials. Internal audit systems required by formal third-party compliance schemes, layered process audits, and consultants or others performing registration review or management reviews may be considered appraisal costs as well. Inspection that is part of standard work is still appraisal cost. Few customers see this as value added work, and some standard costing systems will hide these costs in the product cost structure.

Failure costs are costs resulting from products or services not conforming to requirements or customer/user needs, that is, the costs resulting from poor quality. Failure costs are divided into internal and external failure cost categories:

- *Internal failure* costs occur prior to delivery or shipment of the product or the furnishing of a service. Examples include costs of scrap, rework, re-inspection, re-testing, material review, and downgrading. These costs happen inside the organization's sphere of control and may show up as unplanned and/or non-reimbursed overtime. Scrap may be sold below the cost of creating it, yielding a net loss. The cost to create the scrap usually does not include the extra costs to remove it from the value stream and prepare it for sale as scrap. Not accounting for these costs allows continuance of a scrap system on the assumption that it "pays for itself."

- *External failure costs* occur after delivery or shipment of the product or during or after furnishing of a service. Examples include the costs of processing customer complaints, necessary field service, customer returns, warranty claims, and product recalls. Sometimes third-party inspection is required, premium freight costs are incurred to and from the customer, replacement of poor product reduces capacity and drives more overtime, and so on.

The split between internal and external maybe blurred due to partnership agreements. Typically, the product or service becomes external when income from delivery is booked. This definition must be defined for an individual firm and for individual product/ service lines.

QUALITY COST ELEMENTS

Quality cost elements are the detailed functions, tasks, or expenses which, when properly combined, make up the quality cost *categories*. For example, quality planning is an element of prevention, in-process inspection is an element of appraisal, rework is an element of internal failure, and customer returns are an element of external failure costs.

Although it is recommended that quality cost categories be used as shown here, the elements making up these categories will be different from industry to industry. Quality cost elements in healthcare, for example, will differ significantly from those in manufacturing. Because of the extent of these differences and the many industries involved (for example, banking, insurance, hospitality, and so on), no attempt will be made to provide complete lists of these elements by industry. However, every attempt will be made to include examples from these industries wherever possible in order to help readers develop their own lists. Using the category definitions and examples as guidelines, you can tailor the elements for your organization.

In developing detailed elements for your organization, first describe the activities or work being performed that could be considered quality costs (that is, work that would be unnecessary if quality were always perfect). Then, using the category definitions as a guide, fit these tasks into the proper categories. For example, if the task is being accomplished to prevent poor quality, the cost of the task is a prevention cost.

Some accounting systems excel in measuring all components of cost. In the case of quality costs, a comprehensive effort is not realistic. Since the goal is to drive improvement, using the 80:20 rule here makes it possible to see and fix the major cost elements, bypass minor cost elements, and focus on finding the root causes of the primary drivers of poor quality cost.

Taking the cost of quality from production to the rest of the organization may mean a shift to the "cost of poor execution." Looking at support departments allows the fullest possible benefit of this discipline. It may not be necessary to make this effort at first; expand the effort as the direct production areas see benefits.

Developers of individual quality cost systems will find detailed descriptions of quality cost elements for each category of quality costs in Appendix B; these may be used as a guide. For further help, look to ASQ Quality Press and at the ASQ website, www.asq.org, for excellent articles and publications on quality costs in various service and manufacturing industries.

QUALITY COST BASES (DENOMINATORS)

In working out the details of an individual quality cost system, it is important that the quality manager and the controller work together to mesh their two sources of knowledge into one integrated system. Since the costs involved may be incurred by any department, function, or cost center, a customized internal quality cost procedure is required. This procedure will describe the sources of data to be reported or extracted from the account ledgers in terms of existing account, department, and cost center codes. It will describe how any required estimates are to be prepared and where to use associated labor benefits, allocated costs, and labor burdens. It will provide the measurement bases against which quality costs may be compared.

Actual dollars expended is usually the best indicator for determining where quality improvement projects will have the greatest impact on profit and where corrective action should be taken, but unless the amount of work performed is relatively constant, it will not provide a clear indication of quality cost improvement trends.

Remember, the prime value of a quality cost system is in identifying opportunities for improvement and then providing a measurement of that improvement over time. Since the volume of business in total, or in any particular product or service line, will vary with time, real differences (improvements) in the cost of quality can best be measured as a percent of, or in relation to, some appropriate base or denominator. Total quality cost compared to an applicable base results in an index that may be plotted and periodically analyzed in relation to past indices. The base used should be representative of, and sensitive to, fluctuations in business activity.

For long-range analyses, net sales is the base most often used for presentations to top management. For example, total cost of quality may be scheduled for improvement from 9% of sales to 8% during a given business plan year. While this measurement may be important from a strategic planning point of view, it would not be practical and could be misleading for the day-to-day, week-to-week, or month-to-month needs of the practitioners who are commissioned to make it happen. There may be a large lag between incurring the cost of quality expense and the booking of net sales. Variation in these two out of synchrony with each other will make the ratio vary almost at random. Consequently, this base is best for long-range analysis and tracking.

As an example in aircraft manufacturing, the failure to ship just one aircraft in the quality cost report period could severely impact sales for that period. Sales for the period would drop significantly, thereby causing a rise in the quality cost index although, in fact, quality performance may not have changed at all. Going one step further, we can see that the sale of that aircraft in the following period might inflate that period's sales figures, thereby causing a significant but misleading quality improvement trend when compared to the previous period.

In general, in industries where sales may vary significantly from one quality cost reporting period to another, net sales will not make a good short-term comparison base. However, these short-term sales variations should even out over the long term, and the use of net sales for a long-range comparison base is excellent. Net sales is commonly understood as a volume measure, making it an easy choice for a base.

Short-range bases should be directly related by time and location to quality costs as they are being incurred and reported. They should relate the cost of quality to the amount of work performed. For short-range use, appropriate bases for quality costs are best determined from a review of data already in use in work areas and already understood by the people who will have to learn to use quality costs. In fact, the best bases are those that are already key measures of production. Typical examples include overall operating costs, total or direct labor costs, value added costs, and the actual average cost of delivered product or service. The basic idea is to use a meaningful, on-line, and well-known base relating to the amount of business activity in each area where quality cost measurements are to be applied in support of performance improvement.

Cost of goods sold is often used, as it represents a "cost" basis. Sales represents a "revenue" basis, with all the alterations between cost and revenue. For example, sales may be delayed significantly after cost of production, profit mix in sales can vary in ways that cloud the cost of quality utility, and competitive pricing may create temporary changes inappropriate for an internal metric such as quality cost.

For effective use of a quality cost system, it may be preferable to use more than one base. For long-range planning purposes, total quality costs as a percent of net sales is often used. There may be no better common denominator than net sales for year-to-year planning and measures of accomplishment according to top management. For current, ongoing applications, however, several bases can be used. The bases selected should be related to the management emphasis already being placed on specific areas for improvement. The following examples are typical indices that incorporate this feature:

- Internal failure costs as a percent of total production / service costs
- External failure costs as an average percent of net sales
- Procurement appraisal costs as a percent of total purchased material costs
- Operations appraisal costs as a percent of total production / service costs
- Total quality costs as a percent of production / service costs

There is no limit to the number of indices or the level of detail that an effective quality cost system can have. More danger exists in oversimplification—such as using only one base for all purposes. There is no single perfect base. Each base can be misleading if used alone and this can easily lead to confusion and disinterest. It's important to the success of quality cost use that bases for individual progress measurements not appear to be unnatural to the functional area. Instead, they should be seen as complementary (for example, rework costs as a percent of area labor costs). They could also be used to provide indices that may have shock value, simply to get the corrective action juices flowing (for example, "Hey, did you know that for every dollar expended in your area, 50 cents is the cost of poor quality?").

To help in the selection process, consider the following types of normally available bases:

- A labor base (such as total labor, direct labor, or applied labor)
- A cost base (such as shop cost, operating cost, or total material and labor)
- A sales base (such as net sales billed or sales value of finished goods or services)
- A unit base (such as the number of units produced, the number of services performed, or the volume of output)

OTHER CONSIDERATIONS PERTAINING TO BASES

Additional factors can influence application of these bases.

- **Sensitivity to increases and decreases in production/service schedules.** Most manufacturing and service operations have a level at which efficiency is highest. Additions to and subtractions from the work force, maintenance of equipment, and the use of backup suppliers may influence both quality costs and built-in prime costs. If the influence is substantial, an attempt should be made to quantify these factors and recommend changes to minimize adverse effects. Successful companies use many techniques to overcome such adverse influences, including flexible manufacturing systems, intensive formal training, and Lean quality programs with suppliers.

- **Automation.** With productivity and quality as national goals in the world-class competition for business, successful companies have turned to robotics and automation to reduce direct and indirect costs. Here again, the effects on ratios such as scrap, rework, or appraisal versus direct labor costs may be substantial. Obviously, application of quality cost principles dictates that we be able to measure the (presumed) favorable influence of automation on appraisal or failure costs and, more broadly, on the ability of a business to influence customer perceptions and actual experience concerning quality.

- **Seasonal product sales.** Some companies (for example, department stores), have high seasonal sales. External failure costs such as customer complaints may be seasonally grouped and quality costs adjusted accordingly. A four-quarter moving average of the ratio between external failure costs and net sales billed is an appropriate technique to use in these circumstances.

- **Oversensitivity to material price fluctuations.** The law of supply and demand still prevails and raw material costs may experience wide fluctuations. If internal failure or appraisal ratios result from the application of prime costs, this may have a dramatic effect. In such cases, the use of direct labor (rather than prime costs) may be appropriate.

The possibility of wide interest in a cost of quality measure suggests a wide variety in bases, but also a wide variety in cross-functional team makeup. In addition to operations, quality, and accounting, other groups such as production control, logistics, supply chain, and support areas of operations all are needed to reduce quality costs. All should be a part of the team.

TREND ANALYSIS AND THE IMPROVEMENT PROCESS

Quality costs alone cannot do anything for a company except to illustrate what is being expended in specific areas related to quality and highlight opportunities for cost improvement. To put quality costs to use, it's necessary to organize them in a manner that will support analysis. As previously noted, one way to achieve this is to look at quality costs in ratio with known costs. Use them to raise questions such as these:

- Did you know that for every $100 in shipments, we lose $5 in internal distribution and handling failure costs?

- Did you know that for every $100 spent for material purchases, we must spend $3 for supplier goods inspection?

Questions such as these immediately show the value of quality costs in direct relation to known cost expenditures. The next logical step is to assemble and examine these ratios over time to determine whether the situation being depicted is getting better or worse. Failure costs, in particular, lend themselves to this type of analysis. Supplementing the initial analysis with the best empirical explanations of what can be achieved will become the first step in the projection of reasonable improvement goals. Each individual trend analysis can then be extended into the future, first as a plan with specific goals and then to monitor actual progress against the plan.

There are two types of quality cost trend analyses: long-range and short-range.

Long-range analysis normally views total quality costs over quarters or years. It is used principally for strategic planning and management monitoring of overall progress.

Short-range trend charts are prepared for each company area where individual quality cost improvement goals are to be established. One approach is to simply assign a short-range target to each general operational area. Alternatively, an initiative can become as detailed and sophisticated as the quality management system will support.

Figure 2.1 is a composite example of a long-range quality cost trend chart for a typical organization with sales in the range of $100 million to $200 million. It shows total cost of quality as a percentage of net sales over a period of 10 years. It also shows prevention, appraisal, internal, and total failure costs separately as a percent of sales (external failure costs are shown as the difference—the shaded portion—between internal and total failure costs). The first two years show quality cost history without any knowledge of, or emphasis on, its reduction. The third year is the start of quality cost measurement and use. Years four through nine show actual progress accomplished. Year 10 is a projection of the expected continued progress.

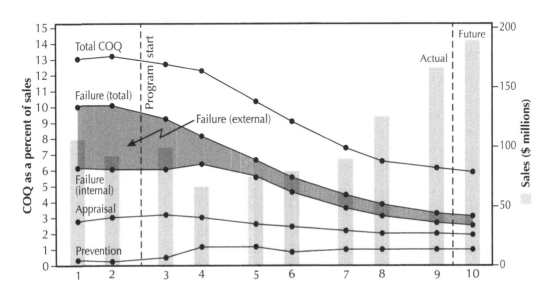

Figure 2.1 Cost of quality history.

To determine exactly where to establish short-range quality cost trend charts and goals, it is necessary to review the company's basic quality measurement system. To actually reduce quality costs, it is necessary to find the root causes of these costs and eliminate them. Real improvement depends on actions within the basic quality measurement and corrective action system, enhanced by the use of quality costs as an important support tool. Specific uses of quality costs, therefore, must be correlated to specific quality measurement target areas for improvement.

A minimum quality measurement system should include summary appraisal results from all key operational areas. These will include receiving inspection, fabrication inspection, final assembly inspection and test, and field failure reports. The summaries are usually presented as trend charts to indicate and make people aware of the current levels of quality performance. Quality cost trend charts, when correlated, will supplement these performance charts with viable cost data to support the improvement effort. This is the essence of their use together (Figure 2.2).

If cost of quality data are correlated with customer's incoming problems or costs, working at cross purposes is avoided and legitimate partnership with a customer can be improved.

It should be noted that there is normally a time lag between basic quality measurement data and quality cost data. Quality measurement data are always current (usually daily), whereas quality cost data are accumulated after the fact as most cost accounting reports are. It is important, therefore, to understand that quality costs are used to support before-the-fact improvement and to verify its after-the-fact accomplishment, but actual improvement originates as a result of using current quality measurement data in the pursuit of cause and corrective action.

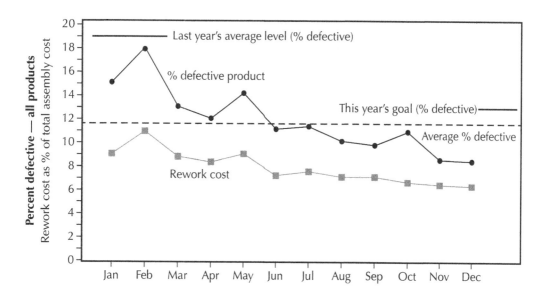

Figure 2.2   Assembly area quality performance.

There is also a time lag between cause and effect (quality improvements do not show immediate reductions in quality cost because of the time lag between the cause and its effect). This lag can be observed on a quality cost trend chart. For this purpose, it may be desirable to indicate on the chart when quality improvements were made. Figure 2.3 is a simplified quality cost trend chart marked to indicate the start of a quality improvement activity. The note enables us to see the reason for the steady improvement over the last five months—in April, training programs were initiated.

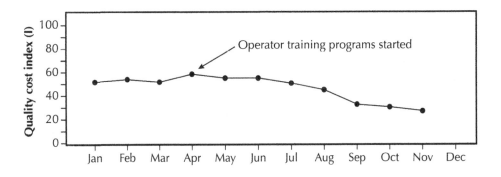

Figure 2.3   Quality cost trend.

The first effect was an increase in the quality cost index due to the cost of the programs (prevention cost increased but failure costs remained the same). After a cause-and-effect lag of about two months, the value of the training became evident as shown by a steady reduction in the quality cost index (failure costs decreased while prevention costs remained the same). By November, a 45% reduction was indicated.

Obviously, the training programs were a worthwhile investment. Had no improvement been indicated after a reasonable amount of time, it would have been necessary to reevaluate the programs and either revise or drop them in favor of some other course of action.

Actual quality improvement begins with the preparation of a cumulative frequency distribution of defect types for each quality performance trend chart utilized. A cumulative frequency distribution can be shown as a simple bar chart using the totals for each defect type for the same time period as the trend being depicted, or a shorter period, as desired. Reorganization of these data in accordance with the Pareto principle (displayed in descending order of significance) will show that only a few of the many contributing types will be responsible for most of the undesired results (Figure 2.4). These "vital few" are identified for investigation and corrective action. In the example shown, 93% of the defects occurred in the drill and tap, plating, and deburring operations. Corrective action concentrated in those operations will have the greatest impact on quality improvement. As each most significant contributor to failure costs is eliminated in descending order, the related failure costs of quality will decline. As each new level of performance is achieved, associated appraisal costs may also be reduced to some degree.

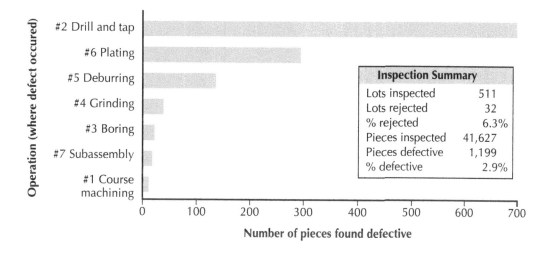

Figure 2.4   Pareto analysis.

The foregoing description of short-range quality cost usage defines a simple, straightforward approach needed by any quality cost program to make it effective. Actual programs can become more complex or sophisticated as required. Fundamentally, if quality costs can be measured and related for an area where basic quality performance data exist, the quality cost improvement process can begin.

For more sophisticated firms, comparing the capability indices of key processes with the costs of non-conforming downstream processes (failure costs) can be made transparent.

In summary, an effective quality cost program consists of the following steps:

1. Establish a quality cost measurement system.

2. Develop a suitable long-range trend analysis.

3. Establish annual improvement goals for total quality costs.

4. Develop short-range trend analyses with individual targets that collectively add up to the incremental demands of the annual improvement goal.

5. Monitor progress against each short-range target and take appropriate corrective action when targets are not being achieved.

6. Determine any potential leading indicators to mitigate COPQ impact before it is incurred.

Chapter 3

Quality Cost Program Implementation

HOW TO GET STARTED

Like many good things in life, a quality cost program will not occur spontaneously: implementation requires an advocate and champion within the company. Although this champion usually is the quality manager (or senior quality function representative), it can be anyone. There are several requirements:

- Knowledge of quality cost systems

- A clear view and belief in their application and value to the company

- Access to and understanding of general ledger and profit and loss statements (to maintain direct financial alignment)

- Desire and willingness to be advocate and leader

- A position within the company providing opportunity to meet the imposed challenges

The first step is to verify with facts that a quality cost program can be beneficial to the company. This is necessary to attract management attention and interest. It will be necessary to conduct an initial review and analysis of financial data in sufficient detail to determine the general levels of quality costs as they exist today. The major costs are important for this purpose. Much of the data required may be readily available. If not, some of these costs may be estimated. The point is that this initial review should be relatively easy and need not account for *all* quality costs. If readily available and easily estimated costs are included and represent the major costs of quality, then sufficient data will have been obtained for presentation to management. These data should justify the effort and interest management in participating in the program. Be careful to locate any major increments of quality cost that may be hidden in large accounts (for example, significant re-work costs buried in normal operating cost accounts).

Once the approximate quality cost levels are determined, the opportunity for improvement should be obvious. The results should be sufficient to sell management on the need for the program. It is not uncommon to find initial

45

quality cost estimates of more than 15% of sales, even in profitable firms. (Remember that sales is not always the best comparison. Cost of goods sold is usually better than sales.) Although direct comparisons cannot be made, some manufacturing companies with extensive quality improvement program and quality cost experience are demonstrating that total quality costs can be reduced to as little as 2% to 4% of sales. This reduction shows as pretax profit.

The next step is to determine whether management is ready to accept and support a quality cost program. Here an internal judgment is required. The real question is whether management is truly open to new ideas in the operations area of the company. Unfortunately, a quality cost program can never succeed from the bottom or the middle of the organization upward. Like all performance improvement programs, success here requires the backing and support of top management.

When it has been determined that top management will be receptive, the next step is to plan the sales pitch needed to achieve its acceptance and support. For this purpose, in addition to the general levels of overall quality costs already determined, a more detailed secondary review will be required. That is, a specific, incremental area of the operation must be exposed to management in sufficient detail to show how actual quality costs can be calculated and eliminated through analysis and corrective action. A secondary review like this helps complete management's understanding of the full cycle of quality cost opportunity and improvement.

A logical approach to finding the right area for a secondary review that can be presented to top management is to conduct a survey looking for specific areas with high failure costs. The areas with the most obvious opportunity for improvement will become apparent. Final selection of the area to be used for secondary review (and probably for pilot and/or first implementation of the ensuing program) requires the involvement of an area management team with a cooperative attitude. The example selected should not only provide the right opportunity but also a high probability of success when the program begins.

If top management is not available, some success has been reported using the MOUND approach ("Middle Out Up aNd Down"). When improvement results driven by middle management and tied to financial impacts are shared upward ("look what I did, boss"), upper management can easily propagate the program laterally to peers who then assign the task analysis to subordinates.

At this point, the champion of quality costs is ready to develop an overall plan and schedule for quality cost program implementation.

Essential ingredients of the plan should include a number of key elements:

- The management presentation, designed to:
  - identify the overall opportunity
  - illustrate how the program will achieve its benefits
  - accomplish management acceptance and support for the implementation plan and schedule

- Conduct of the planned pilot program
- Education of all functions to develop awareness of and interest in participation
- Development of the internal quality cost accounting procedure
- Overall collection and analysis of quality cost data
- Quality cost reporting and use (integration with the quality management system and quality improvement program)

THE MANAGEMENT PRESENTATION

Before undertaking any large-scale attempt to implement a quality cost program, management must be convinced of the value of the program and the use for which the system is intended. Any proposed need for additional efforts in the important business of cost accumulations and use is likely to be challenged. Thus, there is need for a comprehensive presentation to management so as to elicit understanding and interest and justify the proposed effort.

Companies not already engaged in quality cost programs are unaware of the magnitude of the quality cost dollar and its direct impact on their total business. Most businesses are profitable, and management may believe that if business is profitable there is little need to look more closely at expenses. This is where the previous evaluation of the general levels of quality cost comes into play. Those figures not only show the previously unknown levels of quality cost incurred, particularly failure costs, but also the potential cost improvement opportunity. This should whet management's appetite to hear more and allay fears that the proposed benefits may not be real.

As with any selling proposition, it's important to maintain a positive attitude during this presentation and repeatedly stress benefits to management. Not only will current expenses, unproductive work, and pure waste be reduced, but customer relations, market share, employee satisfaction, and profit will be enhanced. There is not a top management team in existence that does not want to improve quality, but there are many that don't know exactly how to proceed or are not sure whether their company can afford it. Some may believe that the returns of a larger investment in quality practices and prevention will not show a sufficient return. The message of cost of quality could be exactly what is needed to justify pursuit of a sound quality improvement program or revise a program that has gone idle.

The presentation should contain a clear description of the detailed intent of the program and how it will be accomplished. It should describe the additional cost data to be gathered (the investment). The quality costs arrived at earlier and the detailed example previously chosen should clearly illustrate that failure costs currently incurred could be almost totally prevented (the return on investment). The picture presented should be one of gold nuggets just sitting there waiting to be plucked from the operation. The clarity and authenticity of this portion of the presentation will go a long way toward alleviating whatever fears management may have about the program's validity. It's helpful to utilize both data or chart imagery and verbal or story imagery. The data tell about magnitudes, the stories tell about values and make a deep connection to strategy. Extension to revenue growth is common. Here is an example statement: "Did you know that for $100 cost of product, we have $10 of cost of poor quality? If we sell for $110 and our competitor sells for $105, what does this do to our sales? How is our cost of making a sale affected? Would a 50% reduction in cost of poor quality position us for a more competitive pricing strategy and increase our business?"

Once management is sold on the genuine value of the program, many firms experience a problem with culture change. This occurs when the leadership gets it, but aspects of established workplace culture hinder development of a quality cost system. There are two steps necessary to overcome this obstacle. First, because culture is often unspoken and therefore unseen, it may be necessary to survey lower-level and middle-level employees to discover the issues. For example, the mere discussion of waste may be avoided due to past experiences. This can become a roadblock to cost-of-quality analysis. In the second step, leaders must question subordinates about these cultural biases to make sure conversations about waste are allowed. After that it is possible to talk about the size of the problem and potential solutions may appear. When these unseen cultural barriers are removed, it's possible to move on to the core concepts of quality costs (Chapter 1) and the need for teamwork among all involved functions. It should be emphasized that quality costs are not solely generated by the quality function but also by design, purchasing, operations, and various support groups. It is indeed a companywide program.

Finally, the presentation should describe the quality cost program implementation plan and schedule, the results that can reasonably be expected, and a clear indication that there will be an extraordinary return on investment. Before the meeting is concluded, management should give its approval, support, and a commitment to participate.

THE PILOT PROGRAM

A pilot program is recommended because it will accomplish a number of important things:

- Prove the ability of the system to produce cost-saving results
- Resell management and influence unsure management on the wider need for the program
- Limit the initial scope of implementation—time, people, and area
- Allow system debugging prior to full implementation

Because of its importance to the ultimate success of quality cost program implementation, the pilot program needs a full-time leader, one who knows quality management and the company and is willing to learn about accounting (a co-leader from accounting would be ideal but is not mandatory). The principal investments in the entire quality cost program are the leader/advocate and the quality cost collection system. This is a relatively small investment in a program that can have far-reaching benefits. It is, however, a point that should have been raised and committed to at the management presentation. Most leaders overestimate the cost of data collection, as technology has improved in this area.

Selection of the pilot area, as discussed previously, should be strongly influenced by the area's potential to produce quick and significant results. Depending upon actual circumstances, it may be advisable to work with a unit as small as a single program or product line within a facility, a typical plant or office in a multi-facility company, or an entire company division. There are no hard-and-fast rules, but the following guidelines should apply. To assure a high probability of success, the unit selected for the pilot program should:

- Be as typical of the company's operation as possible

- Encompass some aspect of either the organization's strategic direction or some issue that has claimed top management's attention

- Identify costs in all categories of quality cost measurement (although some elements may have to be estimated)

- Present obvious improvement opportunities

- Have a cooperative local management

Before starting the detailed planning for the pilot area, a key person from the accounting department should be selected to work part time or full time with the leader/advocate (if a co-leader from accounting was not previously assigned). This person will help bridge the gap between current accounting information and the needs of the pilot quality cost program and will later develop the companywide quality cost accounting procedure. It is advisable to select someone who is quality-minded and a progressive thinker. Select an individual who not only knows how the books should be kept but, more importantly, knows exactly how they are kept. One strong benefit of using someone from accounting is the added buy-in established.

Now the leader/advocate, the accounting representative, and a local area management representative can form a team to pursue the pilot quality cost program objectives. All the expertise needed to assure success exists in this team. From this point on it's a matter of effort, patience, and perseverance.

The pilot program involves these steps:

1. Measurement of quality costs and appropriate bases

2. Tie-in with basic quality measurements

3. Establishment of key trend analysis charts

4. Identification of improvement opportunities and goals

5. Leadership and support to perform problem identification, analysis, and solution

6. Strict enforcement of necessary corrective actions

7. Summary reporting of progress

As the pilot program progresses, it should be documented as a case history for use with quality cost program implementation on a companywide basis. By showing how this "part of the whole" pilot would affect the whole as it is rolled out, visualization of final results is improved. If timing could be such that pilot program progress could be achieved prior to the conclusion of a fiscal year, the stage would be set to allow for companywide implementation to start at the beginning of a new fiscal year.

QUALITY COST EDUCATION

After management approval of the quality cost program and concurrent with the start of the pilot program, key members of each department should be educated in the concepts of a quality cost system and the detailed program plan for implementation. Emphasis should be placed on the involvement of all functions, the importance of team work, and the real opportunities for performance and cost improvement that exist in many functional areas. Most today have had team training, but it does not hurt to do this again. Teamwork is something that often gets left behind in the interests of expediency. In performing a new cross-function activity such as cost of quality, teamwork is important. The importance of examples here cannot be over stressed. The ultimate objective of this education is agreement on the benefits of the program and a commitment to cooperation or participation.

Departments should be given the opportunity to review the entire program as planned and see exactly where they fit. As they come to recognize the contributions or participation that will be expected of them, they can begin to evaluate the program benefits and impact to their individual departments. It is important at this point in program development that all department representatives be encouraged to make program suggestions from their expert viewpoints. Solicit quality cost elements peculiar to each department. Ask them to prepare a list of those tasks or functions performed by their department that can be considered quality costs—work that would not be performed if quality were always perfect. Then, using the definitions provided in Chapter 2 as a guide, fit these tasks into the proper categories—prevention, appraisal, and internal or external failure.

For example, if the function is performed because a product or service did not conform to requirements or customer/user needs, its cost is considered a failure cost. Further, if the nonconformance was discovered prior to delivery or shipment of the product or the furnishing of a service, the failure cost is an *internal* failure cost. (See Figure 3.1 and Appendix B for help in this process.) The tasks or functions listed and categorized are their department's quality cost elements. Adoption of these elements into the program, along with any other worthwhile suggestions, will help to refine the details of the program and allow each department to become a part of the program's development.

As different areas of the company become involved, new quality cost opportunities will become apparent. Some may suggest a revision in data or accounting systems and this may become a roadblock to implementation. To avoid this, search for the "least arguable value" that shows the size of quality costs but does not create a need for extensive system alteration. The focus should be on fixing what is creating waste, not on a fancy measurement system.

The quality cost education of key representatives of involved functional organizations also provides an opportunity to stress their support role to overall quality management, the benefits they will gain from improved quality, and some of the pitfalls that hinder success. The following items should always be included in the quality education of other functions:

- Remember that in the absence of a quality management system and a quality improvement program, there is no need for a quality costs program. Emphasize the twofold benefit of quality improvement—improved customer satisfaction at less cost. Of the five customer types (end user, stakeholder, employee, supplier, and community), most businesses will focus on stakeholder and supplier issues. A robust approach to the COQ system meeting all of these variants will help with a balanced approach.

- Remember that there can be no improvement, cost or otherwise, without corrective action. Each department must be committed to all required corrective action.

- Remember that the objective of the quality cost program is to identify areas where cost improvements can be achieved through the betterment of quality performance. Don't insist that every definable element of quality cost be tracked. If it's not truly significant, don't argue about it. Throw it out.

- Don't complicate the bookkeeping because of quality costs. Relate to it as it is. Change it only if the knowledge gained proves that it should be changed (from a business viewpoint).

- Don't try to move too quickly from the pilot program into all other areas—even when the pilot program is expected to be very successful.

- Accuracy and repeatability are keys to establishing reliability and support for quality costs.

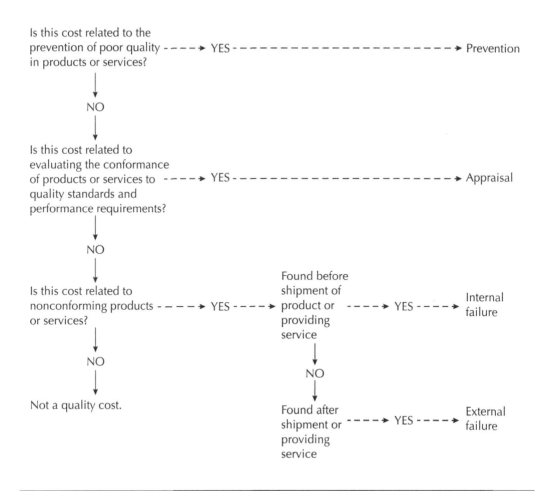

Figure 3.1   Assignment of cost elements to quality cost categories.

INTERNAL QUALITY COST PROCEDURE

Concurrent with progress of the pilot program, the company quality cost procedure can be developed. It will already have been discovered that many of the needed quality cost data are not readily available from the cost accounting system. In a typical service business, for example, many appraisal and internal failure costs are considered a normal part of operations. As such, these costs are not segregated and available for use. In other cases, what is recorded in the accounting books may not be the same as the quality cost definition. Rework in manufacturing, for example, may be accounted for as a variance against a standard allowance. Discrepancies such as these, coupled with expected variation in individual cost accounting systems, clearly signal the need for a detailed, internal quality cost procedure for any company that implements a quality cost program.

The internal quality cost procedure is necessary to describe each element of quality cost to be used and to define how and when the actual cost data are to be estimated or collected and assembled. It also defines the comparison bases to be included. To assure accuracy in terms of actual cost to the company, the procedure should also define the application of fringe benefit costs, overhead burdens, and other accounting adjustments to each defined element of quality cost. Finally, the procedure should establish responsibilities for execution of its requirements and it should provide a reporting format for the quality cost data to be presented for use (see Figure 3.3 for an example of a summary report).

To assure the integrity of quality cost data and their acceptance by all who may be affected by them, the internal procedure should be authorized by the controller or chief accountant. The procedure can be prepared with the help of the quality cost leader/advocate, but it should be implemented through accounting. If the collection of quality cost data is related to the quality function, it will not have the validity required to command attention. In fact, it might easily slip into that realm of accommodations viewed as "belonging to the quality department."

One set of steps used in preparing this procedure may be as follows:

1. Start with the manual of accounts (or chart of accounts or list of ledger accounts). This should provide a description of what each account contains.

2. Use the *Detailed Description of Quality Cost Elements* included in Appendix B to find the formal accounts to use as raw sources.

3. Use the additional element lists arrived at by the individual departments during the quality cost education phase discussed earlier to identify other sources of cost data.

4. Begin matching accounts with quality costs. An obvious match will occur if the account exists only because of less-than-perfect work, such as a rework account. More often than not, the match will not be so obvious and practical judgments will have to be worked out. Internal definitions should use terms that make sense to the users. Use simplification and clarity, rather than magnitude, as the rule of thumb that should be applied. Don't make a "program" out of the collection system.

In preparing the internal procedure, there is no need to agonize over the proper category for any questionable increment of quality cost. Remember that the ultimate aim is to reduce all elements of quality cost consistent with the goals of the company's quality improvement program. With this in mind, increments of quality cost measurements can be allocated to those categories that best fit the needs of the company. This is particularly applicable when a person's normal activities fall in more than one quality cost category, such as a tester who, in addition to acceptance testing, works part time trouble shooting and part time retesting because of failures. In this case a company must decide whether to include the tester's total cost in the appraisal category or to isolate the failure increments of cost (troubleshooting and retesting) based entirely on their value to the company quality cost program. The choice of the "perfect" category is far less important than consistency in execution.

Another problem that may be faced during procedure development is the soundness of key related cost accounting practices. For example, if some waste (scrap) is accounted for but significant amounts are not, the company may decide to tighten up on the definition or practice. If significant costs are being expended because of customer problems and not separately accounted for, the company may decide that now is the time to start accounting for them. The development of each individual quality cost procedure will provide some unique opportunities to refine the cost accounting details for improved financial management.

These improvements in cost reporting may actually cause quality costs to show an increase in the early phases of the program. This must be understood from the beginning to preclude disappointment on the part of management, which may be expecting a windfall cost reduction (see Figure 2.3 and the discussion on cause-and-effect lag in Chapter 2).

Internal company quality cost definitions should be approached in a practical manner. Using Appendix B, Detailed Description of Quality Cost Elements, as a guide, each company should tailor these definitions to meet its own needs (see discussion on quality cost elements in Chapter 2). With experience, quality cost elements can be created, deleted, or combined. There is no single right answer for quality cost systems. Each system should harmonize to the greatest extent possible with the company cost accounting system, and it should be tailored to suit the actual quality improvement opportunities within the company.

QUALITY COST COLLECTION AND ANALYSIS

Preparing and officially issuing the internal quality cost procedure shows a company's commitment to implementation and use of a quality cost system. This is one of the best things that could happen for the quality management program—and for the quality manager.

Quality Cost Collection

Ideally, the internal quality cost procedure includes a complete system of cost elements. These cost elements (or accounts) should be coded in such a way that the costs of prevention, appraisal, and internal and external failures could be easily distinguished and sorted. The cost elements described in Appendix B are coded in such a fashion. This is easily seen in the Detailed Quality Cost Element Summary (Figure B.1) in Appendix B.

Using such a coding system, the sum of all cost element codes beginning with 1 would be the total prevention cost. In like manner, the sum of elements coded 2 would be the total appraisal cost, and so on. If more detail is desired, the second digit in the cost element code could represent a breakout of further significance. For example, all the 1.3 codes in Appendix B represent prevention costs pertaining to purchasing. Additional digits could be added to the codes depending upon the level of detail desired.

Collection of quality cost data for labor becomes relatively easy with a system such as the one just described. Applicable quality cost element codes are entered on a labor distribution, charge, time card, or data entry system together with the hours expended against the cost elements represented by the codes. The labor hours are subsequently handled by the firm's operational software. An exception to this is scrap. You don't know you are making scrap while you are making it. The work must first be inspected, rejected, and dispositioned before it becomes scrap. In many companies, scrap reporting documents are forwarded to the estimating department, where labor and material costs expended to the stage of completion are estimated. This differs from what is generally termed "replacement cost," or the cost of the work if the job had been completed. We are only interested here in the labor and material dollars actually lost in the work accomplished up to the time of the work being scrapped.

Quality Cost Analysis

Along with the implementation of a system for collecting quality costs, a spreadsheet is prepared listing the elements of quality cost to be collected against a spread of the departments, areas, and/or projects where the costs will occur (Figure 3.2). This will be used by accounting for each reporting period and will show what quality cost elements are being reported (or not being reported) by each reporting area. The next step is to collate the collected costs onto a second sheet (or tab, in a workbook) designed to summarize the data in exact accordance with plans for use (Figure 3.3). It is in these forms that the quality cost data will normally be presented to the quality department for use.

Spreadsheets allow maximum start-up flexibility and do not require extensive programming skill. Finding mistakes in the data flow and calculations is easier with a spreadsheet than in hard-coded solutions, although this comes with some loss of speed. After a quality cost program has been in place for a while and is found to be stable, a more efficient programming solution may be called for. On the other hand, some measurement systems are in a constant state of flux as new priorities are identified. A spreadsheet may be the ideal method to summarize and analyze the cost of quality data in such a dynamic environment.

Initially, the data presented will be analyzed over a sufficient period of time, in conjunction with basic quality measurement data, to determine and verify current opportunities for improvement. As part of overall quality improvement efforts these opportunities will be presented to the work groups involved for their understanding and commitment to problem identification, cause determination, and necessary corrective action. At this point, improvement targets can and should be established.

Remembering that quality costs are a support tool to the quality management program, it should be clear that further uses of quality cost data will be integral to the prime quality management or quality improvement program. Normally, the data will be used to develop individual trend charts to depict the initial opportunity, the targets for improvement, and actual progress against the targets (Figure 3.4). The data are also used to prepare overall progress charts (usually monthly or quarterly) for subsequent use with quality management reports (Figure 3.5).

Element Code	Description	Accounting	Administration	Engineering	Estimating	Field services	Manufacturing engineering	Marketing	Procurement	Production	Production control	Quality	Receiving	Shipping	Totals
1.1.1	Marketing research														
1.1.2	Customer/user perception surveys/ clinics														
1.1.3	Contract/document review														
1.2.1	Design quality progress reviews														
1.2.2	Design support activities														
1.2.3	Product design qualification test														
1.2.4	Service design — qualification														
1.2.5	Field trials														
1.3.1	Supplier reviews														
1.3.2	Supplier rating														
1.3.3	Purchase order tech data reviews														
1.3.4	Supplier quality planning														

Figure 3.2   Quality cost data spreadsheet.

Quality Cost Summary Report

for the month ending _____

(in thousands of U.S. dollars)

Description	Current month			Year to date		
	Quality costs	As a percent of		Quality costs	As a percent of	
		Sales	Other		Sales	Other
1.0 Prevention costs						
1.1 Marketing/customer/user						
1.2 Product/service/design development						
1.3 Purchasing prevention costs						
1.4 Operations prevention costs						
1.5 Quality administration						
1.6 Other prevention costs						
Total prevention costs						
Prevention targets						
2.0 Appraisal costs						
2.1 Purchasing appraisal costs						
2.2 Operations appraisal costs						
2.3 External appraisal costs						
2.4 Review of test and inspection data						
2.5 Misc. quality evaluations						
Total appraisal costs						
Appraisal targets						
3.0 Internal failure costs						
3.1 Product/service design failure costs						
3.2 Purchasing failure costs						
3.3 Operations failure costs						
3.4 Other internal failure costs						
4.0 External failure costs						
Total failure costs						
Failure targets						
Total quality costs						
Total quality targets						

Base data	Current month		Year to date		Full year	
	Budget	Actual	Budget	Actual	Budget	Actual
Net Sales						
_____ Other base (specify)						

Figure 3.3   Quality cost summary report.

One of the biggest pitfalls to avoid in the implementation of a quality cost program is approaching it from a stand-alone point of view. Quality cost reports, even total quality costs, can have no meaning without the benefit of a meaningful dialogue about actual company performance.

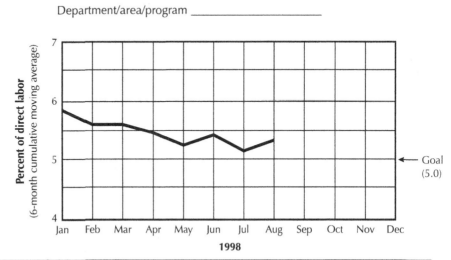

	Jan	Feb	Mar	Apr	May	Jun	Jul	Aug	Sep	Oct	Nov	Dec
Total quality cost*	937.9	921.8	1380.5	1217.2	888.9	1385.5	1157.5	1290.7				
Direct labor	16,429	18,984	25,028	21,051	18,562	25,363	24,546	20,943				
% of direct labor	5.7	4.9	5.5	5.8	4.8	5.5	4.7	6.2				
6-month moving average	5.8	5.6	5.6	5.5	5.3	5.4	5.2	5.4				

*In thousands

Figure 3.4   Total quality costs.

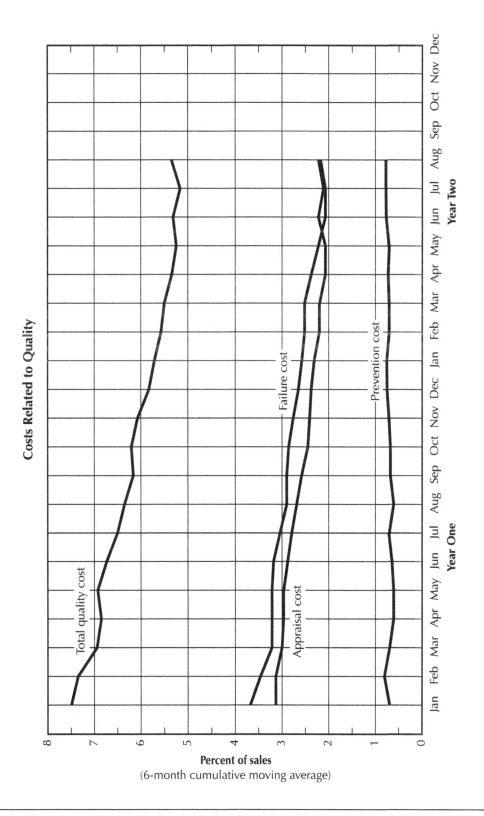

Figure 3.5   Costs related to quality.

ACTIVITY BASED COSTING

Quality Costs and the Accounting Department

Once an organization decides to identify, collect, and monitor its quality costs, it usually turns to the accounting department and says, in effect, "Find me all the costs of quality" or "Tell me what we are spending on prevention, appraisal, and failure." The accounting department normally comes back and says, "Wait a minute! That's not the way we collect our costs. We don't have accounting buckets called 'prevention' or 'appraisal' or 'failure.' We don't collect costs in such categories." So the next job is usually for a quality specialist to sit down with a member of the accounting department and together scan the existing accounting categories to identify those accounts that represent or contain costs that are quality related. Sometimes this is relatively simple and straightforward. For example, there may be an inspection department whose total budget represents appraisal activities. Or there may be cost variances or overruns caused by failure to meet a deadline due to a quality problem.

Often quality costs are not so easily identified. In most cases, significant quality costs lie buried, typically in standard cost, and must be uncovered. Standard cost is the anticipated average planned cost in the manufacture of a product or delivery of a service. It consists of direct labor, direct materials, and overhead (see Appendix A). For example, standard cost for a product may be based on a historical 90% yield, which means that about 10% of the standard cost represents scrap. A 10% scrap level is planned. The cost of scrap would show in the accounting ledger only if it exceeded the planned 10% and would appear as a cost overrun. The quality specialist and the representative of the accounting department must devise new accounting categories to identify the real cost of scrap or rework.

Enter ABC

Although quality costs can be identified and collected within the framework of any financial accounting system, one accounting method is particularly compatible with quality cost methodology and objectives. Activity Based Costing (ABC) aims to improve overall cost effectiveness through a focus on key cost elements. Quality cost methodology seeks to assign quality related costs to specific activities, products, processes, or departments so that these costs can be targeted for reduction. The use of ABC techniques makes it easier to find and assign these costs. The level of detail and the information content inherent in conventional accounting practices are often insufficient for adequate quality cost analysis and application to continuous improvement. ABC, on the other hand, because of its more detailed cost data base, is better suited to these needs.

Activity Based Costing is an accounting procedure for allocating the cost of indirect and overhead expenses (the cost of an organization's resources) to specific activities in proportion to the use of a given resource by that activity. This is in contrast to conventional accounting practice, which allocates indirect and overhead expenses in proportion to direct costs incurred by an activity. In the sections that follow, we shall see through examples the implications of this accounting difference and how ABC can facilitate the use of quality costs to achieve continuous quality improvement.

Conventional means of allocating indirect or overhead costs often create a standard cost where labor costs are grossly inflated. By the inclusion of non value added steps such as waiting for missing assembly parts to arrive or waiting for information to fulfill an order in a retail operation, both cycle time and "assigned" cost or standard cost are increased.

To make quality costs work in this environment, someone must break down the labor costs for assembling a product into those representing activities that are essential (for example, soldering a lead) and those that do not add value (for example, moving a batch of circuit boards into storage). The breakout of quality costs, while not always easy, is at least conceptually sound.

This would work with labor and materials that are closely tied to the actual production. What about other costs?

How Overhead Costs Are Assigned to Products or Services

Some costs can be assigned directly to specific units of product or service. These typically are the cost of labor hours expended or the cost of incoming materials or energy consumed to produce a unit of output. These are called "direct costs" and at one time represented by far the largest fraction of the cost of a product or service. Other costs are not closely tied to direct labor and are usually called "overhead." These fall into three categories:

- Cost of setting up production for a batch of product or shipping or receiving multiple lots of product (depends on batch or lot size)

- Activities that fall into the category of support services for several products or services (complaint handling, purchasing, shipping materials, perishable tools, supervisors, maintenance)

- Expenses incurred at the facility level that must be paid regardless of output (such things as property taxes, depreciation of plant, insurance, rent, warranties, and so on)

Overhead costs in conventional accounting practice are incorporated into standard cost in proportion to the amount of direct labor (or sometimes in proportion to machine hours or direct materials) already contained in the standard cost (that is, consumed in providing a unit of output). The more direct labor involved in providing a product or service, the more overhead expense is assigned to that product or service. When direct labor content is used to apportion overhead costs, the direct labor can be said to be a "cost driver."

To better grasp this idea of overhead cost allocation, let's consider an example of a plant that manufactures two products, "shafts" and "housings," and see how an indirect expense, "material handling," is assigned using conventional accounting methods. Later, we will look at how activity based costing would assign this cost, and discuss how these affect the measurement of quality costs. The example is illustrated in Figure 3.6, which represents one month of data.

Direct labor hours = 10,000
Total direct labor cost @ $15 per hour = $150,000
Labor content of shafts and housing = 0.25 hours

Number of loads transported = 1200
Material handling expense @ $10 per load = $12,000
Material handling requirement:
      Shafts = 2 loads per 100-piece lot
      Housings = 4 loads per 100-piece lot

Figure 3.6   Material handling monthly expense data.

The monthly material handling expense is $12,000. Since there are 10,000 hours of direct labor expended in the plant each month, each direct labor hour also carries a material handling overhead charge of $1.20 per hour.

[$12,000 / 10,000 hours = $1.20 per hour]

The direct labor content of these two products is identical at 0.25 direct labor hours; each shaft and housing therefore is allocated $0.30 material handling charge.

[0.25 hours x $1.20 per hour = $0.30 (shaft or housing)]

This is the conventional allocation. We know there is more material handling involved in transporting the shafts (four loads for housings vs. two loads for shafts) and we choose to live with the misallocation, since everything comes out right in the end (at shipping and billing).

As we measure quality costs, we could start by adding indirect costs to the costs of defective shafts and housings. This would overstate the defect cost for shafts and understate the defect cost of housings. If defects were more common in shafts (due to complexity or process), overall quality costs would be misstated and projects might be set up to improve the wrong work process. A large misdirected effort would result.

Example with Activity Based Costing

With ABC, costs of resources are assigned to activities in proportion to the use of the particular resource by each activity. In the example, the $12,000 monthly cost of material handling is allocated as $10.00 to each load.

[$12,000 / 1200 loads carried = $10.00 per load]

The number of loads transported becomes the "cost driver," in contrast to the direct labor content. It requires four loads (@ $10.00 per load, or $40.00) to transport a 100-piece lot of housings and only two loads (@ $10.00 per load, or $20.00) to transport a 100-piece lot of shafts. A material handling cost of $0.40 is allocated to the cost of producing a housing; a cost of $0.20 is allocated to the manufacture of a shaft.

[$40.00 / 100 housings = $0.40 per housing]

[$20.00 / 100 shafts = $0.20 per shaft]

This is a more accurate assignment of costs than found in conventional accounting practice. In this case, one defective housing or one defective shaft carries the correct cost. Using these quality costs to direct problem solving will set the effort in the right direction.

Conventional accounting methods have worked in the past because overhead costs were a small portion of total cost. This is no longer true. With automation and computer controlled processes, direct costs are overshadowed by indirect costs and other overhead expenses. It is not uncommon for overhead rates to be several times that of direct labor costs. Poorly allocated overhead makes our metrics (including quality cost analysis) show the wrong things. To have a hope of controlling and reducing costs, we need to see what is really going on, and what it is costing us.

In the example above, material handling, and specifically the number of loads transported, is a cost driver. In reality there are many cost drivers— purchase orders, machine setups, complaint investigations, maintenance calls, engineering changes, lost items, and more. For each cost driver, an overhead rate is determined by dividing total costs for the driver (for example, total costs for all complaint investigations) by the number of driver events (the number of complaints investigated). The results might be, for example, $70 per machine setup, $850 per complaint investigation, $165 per maintenance call. These rates can then be applied to specific products or services, recognizing that different products utilize various components of overhead at different levels and in some cases may not utilize them at all. For example, if it costs $850 to investigate a complaint and there are 10 customer complaints associated with shafts in a given month, then ABC requires an assignment of $8500 of the overall customer complaint expense to shafts for that time period.

All of this seems like a lot more work for the accounting office. At one time that would have been true, but with the computerization that now exists in all state-of-the-art accounting departments, it is only the initial setup of accounts that requires more accounting work. After that everything is automatic and, assuming proper data entry, accurate detailed cost information is available upon request.

Using Activity Based Costing to Identify and Analyze Quality Costs

While ABC makes possible more accurate assignment of all overhead costs and can lead, for example, to more correct product or service pricing, it offers a special benefit in the area of quality costs, namely the better identification of those activities that can lead to quality improvement. For example, in the case of customer complaints, we are already talking about a quality cost (external failure). It is important for purposes of problem solving and continuous improvement that we know what portion of the customer complaint cost is assignable to shafts as opposed to housings.

In conventional accounting practice we can always get this information by going to the customer service department and sorting through complaint records. This effort is multiplied many times over when we consider the number of products and the number of quality cost types.

In addition, it would be necessary to repeat this task at regular intervals (for example, monthly). In activity based accounting, this breakout has already been done for us. Moreover, the process that identifies and quantifies the many cost drivers in an organization provides a data base that not only lets us find and properly assign quality costs, but also helps us to take apart these quality costs so that we can go from costs to cost drivers, and from cost drivers to drivers of cost drivers, and ultimately to root causes.

By working backward into the allocation formula, we can assign a quality cost to a root cause of a quality problem. This proves extremely valuable since we can then calculate the return on investment and the payback time for an investment to fix a root cause. Let's use the "shafts and housings" example to illustrate this type of analysis.

From Cost Drivers to Root Causes

In our organization, activity based costing is used to allocate overheads. An internal failure cost of $24,000 has been identified for a given year associated with the manufacture of their two products, shafts and housings. This internal failure cost is a result of reworking product, which accounts for $9600 or 40% of the internal failure cost, and of scrapping product, which accounts for $14,400 or 60% of the internal failure cost. For various reasons, different percentages of shafts could be reworked as compared to housings, and hence the percentages scrapped are also different for the two products. Rework and scrap are cost drivers in ABC terms.

Figure 3.7 shows how costs are assigned to the two products, shafts and housings, in proportion to the extent that each product consumes that driver (uses rework resources or accounts for scrap). But the analysis need not stop here, because we can investigate the causes for rework and scrap for both products. These causes are also shown in Figure 3.7. These are drivers of drivers or second-order drivers. We see a total of seven different causes

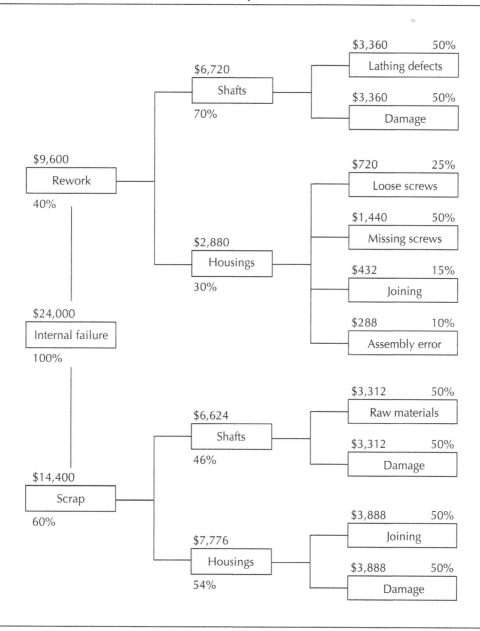

Figure 3.7   Internal failure costs breakdown — shafts and housings.

distributed among the two products accounting for either rework or scrap. We can divide the costs of rework and scrap into the costs associated with the factors responsible for the rework and scrap.

The costs attributable to each cause are shown in Figure 3.7 and summarized in Figure 3.8, where they are also displayed in Pareto fashion. From a quality improvement perspective, the biggest payback would result from finding the causes of "damage" and correcting them. This might require the identification of another level of causes and cost drivers. Some drivers will prove to be root causes.

Given the level of cost detail available from ABC, it is possible to estimate the cost impact of fixing a cause. In the example cited, $10,560 is a result of "damage" to both shafts and housings. If 75% of the damage could be eliminated through identifying and correcting root causes, a savings of $7920 per year would result. The estimated savings can then be compared to the required investment. In the example, an investment of $4000 would have a payback period of approximately six months ($4000/$7920). The level of detail inherent in activity based costing enables cost–benefit analysis and provides for sound investment decision making for continuous quality improvement.

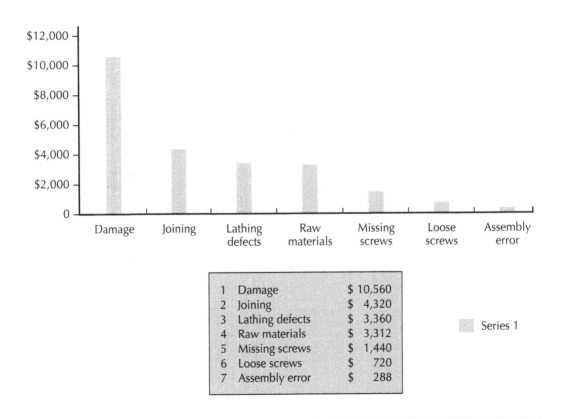

1	Damage	$ 10,560
2	Joining	$ 4,320
3	Lathing defects	$ 3,360
4	Raw materials	$ 3,312
5	Missing screws	$ 1,440
6	Loose screws	$ 720
7	Assembly error	$ 288

Figure 3.8 Failure categories.

Conclusion

Although the greater level of detail in ABC may make it easier, quality cost separation can be done using conventional cost accounting data accompanied by judicious decisions about what is waste. The situation changes when it comes to overhead costs. Using conventional accounting procedures when direct cost is relatively small often leads us into doing things that really don't make sense in assigning overhead costs.

The use of activity based costing in conjunction with quality cost analysis offers several advantages:

1. Overhead costs, which may represent by far the largest portion of the cost of a product or service, can be accurately broken down and assigned to the product, department, process, or activity that is responsible for these costs. The automation of cost systems has greatly reduced the cost of obtaining more accurate information characteristic of activity based costing.

2. A great many quality costs are in the overhead category rather than in the direct costs category. This is particularly true of "hidden" quality costs, those intangible costs that do not fit our conventional categories of rework, scrap, warranties, and so on. (See discussion of hidden quality costs on pages 5–7.) With ABC they may be accurately assigned.

3. With the proper assignment of overhead costs, the calculation of the cost of poor quality changes and often affects the identification of the vital few areas for quality improvement. This impacts project selection and investment decisions.

4. Distinctions between high performing departments or processes and low performing departments or processes, with respect to quality, become more obvious when overhead is properly allocated.

5. The changes in quality costs over time can be more realistically gauged when the artifacts of arbitrarily assigned overhead costs are eliminated.

6. Non-value added and non-cost effective activities can be more readily identified and eliminated, thus leading to improvements in cycle time as well as quality and costs.

Chapter 4

Use of Quality Costs

QUALITY IMPROVEMENT AND QUALITY COSTS

Once the quality cost system is installed, its principal use is to justify and support quality performance improvement in each major area of product or service activity. Performance improvement starts with the identification of problems. In this context, a problem is defined as an area of high quality cost. Every problem thus identified is an opportunity for profit improvement because every dollar saved in the total cost of quality is directly translatable into a dollar of pretax earnings.

Chapter 5, Quality Improvement and Reducing Quality Costs, describes techniques for using quality cost data in programs to improve quality, reduce costs, and thereby improve profits. Chapter 5 clearly identifies that effective use of quality costs analysis means full integration with the quality measurement and corrective action system. Fundamentally, quality cost measurements are established for each major product/service line or cost center within the total operation. As these measurements become an integral part of the quality measurement system, coupled with the identification and elimination of the causes of defects, they logically come to provide the language for improvement potential and goals.

Actual progress in quality improvement and quality cost reductions cannot be delivered by fiat; it must be earned through the hard work process of problem solving. There are many methods for the analysis of quality data, but it also requires knowledge of company operations and the processes involved. Knowledge of basic statistics and problem-solving techniques is also important. Once a cause in need of correction is identified, the action necessary must be carefully determined, and it must be individually justified on the basis of an equitable cost tradeoff (for example, a $200 per week rework problem versus a $5,000 solution). At this point, experience in measuring quality costs will be invaluable in estimating the true payback for individual corrective action investments. Cost–benefit justification of corrective action is an ongoing part of the quality management program.

It should be recognized that the generation of errors and defects is not limited to operations personnel. Errors that result in waste and rework are often caused by product/service and process design engineers, by the designers and fabricators of tools and operating equipment, by those individuals who determine process capabilities, and by those who provide the written instructions for the operator. Also, errors that affect product or service can be caused by the calibration technician, the maintenance person, or even material handlers. Clearly, almost anyone within the total operation can contribute to failure costs. Effective corrective action, therefore, can and will take many avenues throughout the operating organization.

For some, an alternate definition of quality costs is preferred. Offered by Dale and Plunkett (1995)[1] and referenced in the 2006 paper by Schiffauerova and Thomson,[2] this definition encompasses a broader view: "...the costs incurred in the design, implementation, operation and maintenance of a quality management system, the cost of resources committed to continuous improvement, the costs of system, product, and service failures, and all other necessary costs and non-value added activities required to achieve a quality product or service."

Some problems have fairly obvious solutions and can be fixed immediately (for example, replacement of a worn machine bearing or a worn tool). Others are not so obvious, such as a marginal condition in design or processing, and these are almost never discovered and corrected without the benefit of a well-organized and formal approach supported by related costs. Marginal conditions often result in problems that become lost in the accepted cost of doing business. Having an organized corrective action system justified by quality costs will cause such problems to surface for management review and demand for action.

The thing to remember about corrective action is that you only have to pay for it once, whereas failure to take corrective action must be paid for over and over again.

Another important use of quality costs analysis is as an integral part of quality management reporting. Quality management reports are used to report quality progress and to focus attention on areas needing improvement. They are used to inform management of overall status and, in a more direct manner, to promote and support needed action in each major area. Without quality cost as a focal point for demanding action and reporting progress, quality management reporting would be a more difficult task. There is no better way to measure the overall success of the quality improvement program. If improvement is being achieved, problems are being resolved and quality costs are being reduced.

When quality costs are used in management reports, caution should be exercised in attempting to compare different product/service lines or operations areas. People inexperienced in the ways of quality costs probably will have a tendency to compare complex operations with relatively simple ones and expect similar results. This can never be. Areas pushing state-of-the-art and new activities in general will have higher quality costs as a percentage of some base than mature, well-performing operations. There is always a danger in comparing quality costs. It pays to keep the focus on reduction, regardless of starting level.

QUALITY COSTS AND THE STRATEGIC BUSINESS PLAN

One mission of the quality management function is to educate top management about the long-range effects of total quality performance on the profits and quality reputation of the company. Management must become convinced that strategic planning for quality is as essential as planning for any other functional area. Unless the ingredient of quality is truly built into company operations, from the first concept of a new product or service to the ultimate satisfaction of its users, all of which may take years, a company cannot be truly confident about the degree of actual customer satisfaction that will be achieved.

A variety of programs have been implemented to solve issues at many organizations. The type applied depends on the organization's need. To make these approaches clear, a corresponding variety of systems have emerged. Balanced scorecards, enterprise resource planning, customer relationship management systems, activity based costing, process improvement steering committees, and custom information systems seek to help show the progress of improvement. Six Sigma and Lean programs (these may be placed under the umbrella of enterprise performance management) still need a means to apply financial measurements to verify their global impact and to keep their focus on the wider organizational opportunities for improvement. Cost of quality analysis is the tool for making enterprise performance improvement a key strategic element for top level executives.

The strategic planning process focuses on costs. It is management's way of substantiating future profits. Because it is cost oriented, the cost of quality analysis allows the quality function to readily meet the challenge of inclusion in this most important planning activity for the company. Attention to quality costs allows the effect of the management of quality to be cost quantified. It further allows quality costs to be considered in the plans and budgets for each department or area where they occur. Thus, quality cost systems can be viewed as the link that allows the quality function to become a bona fide member of the company's (cost-oriented) management team.

The strategic planning process involves, in general, a review and analysis of past performance and present position; establishment of business objectives based on actual current or anticipated conditions; election of specific, strategic action plans to achieve the objectives; and the implementation and monitoring phase. The quality function's role in this process should be to:

- Analyze major trends in customer satisfaction, defects or error rates, and quality costs, both generally and by specific program or project. These trends should also be used to provide inputs for setting objectives.

- Assist other functions to ensure that costs related to quality are included in their analyses for setting objectives.

- Develop an overall quality strategic plan that incorporates all functional quality objectives and strategic action plans, including plans and budget for the quality function.

There is no better way for the quality management function to "put its stake in the ground" than to develop a strategic quality plan substantiated by quality costs, and to have this plan committed to in the overall company business plan.

SUPPLIER QUALITY COSTS

Supplier quality costs, if tracked, can be significant and can be good indicators of problem areas. A system of managing and tracking supplier quality costs follows the methods discussed for quality costs in general. They, too, are categorized as prevention, appraisal, and failure costs as defined in Chapter 2. Supplier quality costs include prevention cost elements such as the cost of supplier quality surveys; appraisal cost elements such as the costs of receiving and source inspection; and failure cost elements such as the cost of dealing with nonconforming purchased material, the costs of scrap and rework of supplier-caused nonconformances, and the cost of site visits to correct supplier service problems.

Hidden Supplier Quality Costs

Some supplier quality costs are apparent and it's relatively easy for the buyer to identify and assign them to specific suppliers, as in the examples just mentioned. Other supplier quality costs are hidden, just as there are hidden quality costs in any quality cost system (see Chapter 1).

Hidden supplier quality costs fall into one of three parts:

1. Those incurred by the supplier at the supplier's facility.

2. Those incurred by the buyer in solving problems at the supplier's facility.

3. Those costs not usually allocated to suppliers but incurred by the buyer as a result of potential or actual supplier problems.

Quality costs incurred by the supplier at his facility are unknown to the buyer and, therefore, hidden. Even though the magnitude is hidden, the types of costs are not. They are the same types of quality costs the buyer incurs. For example, the supplier certainly has prevention efforts. If he makes a product, he has expenses related to the quality engineering of the product. Even if the supplier is a small shop, this task must be done by someone and may very well be handled by the production supervisor if the plant lacks a quality engineering staff. Certainly effort is expended in the appraisal area, even by the smallest suppliers. Someone must inspect the product or service prior to delivery. (In a small shop, this is done by the operator who made the item.) Each shop, whether large or small, has failure costs. A supplier who makes a mistake in manufacturing must either rework the item or scrap it, creating an internal failure cost. If the supplier sends an imperfect item to the buyer it may be rejected, creating an external failure cost for the supplier. If the supplier is performing a service and the buyer is not satisfied, the supplier can either redo the work or replace the original product with a new one (for example, a dry cleaner can replace a ruined garment), both external failure costs.

The second type of hidden cost, that which is incurred by the buyer in solving problems at the supplier's facility, is usually not specifically allocated to suppliers. Except for an awareness of troubled suppliers, there is usually no tabulation of the cost of the effort or the travel expenses involved. Therefore, the actual expense is hidden. An example is the cost to the buyer of sending a quality engineer to a supplier to resolve a crisis.

The last type of hidden quality cost occurs at the buyer's facility. This type of cost may include the following:

- Specifying and designing gauges that must be used by the buyer's receiving inspection and perhaps by the supplier prior to shipping

- Designing appropriate specifications that the supplier must follow in the manufacture of the product or performance of the service

- Special inspection operations and quality control effort in the buyer's production line related specifically to a supplier product

- Reviewing test and inspection data on supplier material to determine acceptability for processing in the buyer's facility

- Calibrating and maintaining equipment necessary in the quality control of supplier material

- Lost production time due to unavailability of good material

- Field engineering required to analyze and correct a problem caused by a supplier

These examples of supplier-related hidden costs do not exhaust all the possibilities. There are many more, some of which will be significant in individual situations.

APPLICATION OF QUALITY COSTS TO SUPPLIER CONTROL

Provided a buyer has progressed beyond just asking suppliers for price reductions to keep the business, the buyer must determine which supplier-related quality costs are to be reduced. Comparing the relative magnitude of quality costs by category and element should be the first step. The buyer company's quality cost program could be an invaluable aid to accomplish this analysis. For example, assume a situation in which purchased material rejections are the buyer's biggest problem. If the buyer has reason to believe that quality costs will be lowered through improvements in the purchased material rejection rate, it is an important issue for this company.

A Pareto analysis (see Chapter 5) is likely to determine that a relatively few suppliers are causing most of the problems. Now the buyer can focus effort on the "vital few" suppliers and take appropriate action.

What is appropriate action? The buyer might convince the vital few suppliers to institute quality cost programs, if practical for them. Discretion must be exercised before insisting on this. Some companies may be too small to support a quality cost program. Special circumstances may exist in other companies that would prohibit this action. However, if a supplier finds that launching such a program is feasible, the quality costs visible to the buyer most likely will be reduced. If these costs are reduced via root cause analysis, the hidden costs expended by both the buyer and the vital few suppliers will also be lowered. The result will be quality improvement of both the supplier's product/service and the buyer's product/service. This should increase profits for both, and improved profitability for the supplier may eventually result in lower prices for the buyer in a competitive market.

What other action can be taken if we know the magnitude of supplier quality costs? It is possible that these costs can be incorporated into a buyer's supplier rating system. In addition to the traditional inputs of price, delivery, and incoming rejection rate, the supplier rating system should also incorporate supplier quality costs as described in the following example.

A Supplier Rating Program Using Quality Costs

One electrical products manufacturer has been successful with the application of quality costs analysis in a supplier rating program that has been in operation for several years. Although not perfect, this system has proven its effectiveness in improving supplier quality and it is an outstanding example of a practical and workable approach. The company actually uses a dual supplier rating system. The first part is quite traditional in that it tracks price and delivery; that will not be discussed here. The second part, however, evaluates a supplier quality cost performance index (QCPI) based on the following formula:

$$\text{QCPI} = \frac{\text{Supplier Quality Cost} + \text{Purchased Cost}}{\text{Purchased Cost}}$$

No attempt was made to include all supplier quality costs because of administrative problems involved. Only those costs that were important for this particular company were identified.

Cost of Processing Incoming Rejections

Through a study it was determined that each rejected lot of material required approximately $200 of expense to document and return to the supplier. Therefore, the total cost of a supplier's rejected shipments over a period of time was estimated to be the number of rejected lots for the supplier multiplied by $200.

Example

2 Rejected Lots × $200/Rejected Lot = $400

Cost of Complaint Investigations

A special study of the time needed to investigate complaints showed that this could not be estimated to any degree of accuracy. Therefore, each engineer was asked to document the investigation time required for each supplier. The total cost of complaint investigations was estimated to be the investigation time for that supplier multiplied by the average hourly wages and fringe benefits of an engineer.

Example

$$10 \text{ Hours Investigation Time} \times \$40 = \$400$$

Cost of Processing in Receiving Inspection

Because this company had labor standards in receiving inspection, this cost could be estimated by using the appropriate labor standard, the average hourly wages and fringe benefits of a receiving inspector, and the number of lots processed for a particular supplier.

Example

$$1.00 \text{ Std. Hour/Lots} \times \$20/\text{Hour} \times 50 \text{ Lots} = \$1000$$

Cost of a Defective Product after Receiving Inspection

This was difficult to evaluate, because a defective product could be either reworked or scrapped. If scrapped, the cost might not be recovered from the supplier if responsibility could not be clearly assigned. Also, sorting the remaining parts in the lot might be the best alternative. Fortunately, a study indicated that no matter what action was taken, the purchased cost of that part provided an acceptable estimate of the quality costs incurred. Therefore, this cost was estimated for each supplier by multiplying the number of defective parts found after receiving inspection by the initial purchase price of the part.

Example

$$100 \text{ Rejected Parts} \times \$2.80 \text{ Purchased Price/Part} = \$280$$

Caution: This method of estimating the cost of a defective product should not be adopted before verifying by a special study that it is reasonable under your specific circumstances.

Supplier Quality Cost

This company's quality cost for the supplier in question equals the sum of four costs:

Processing incoming rejections	=	$400
Complaint investigations	=	400
Processing in receiving inspection	=	1000
Defective product alter receiving inspection	=	280
Supplier quality cost	=	$2,080

This is a ranking of businesses supplying similar parts by quality cost performance index:

Supplier	Supplier Quality Cost($)	Purchased Cost($)	Index (QCPI)
A	2,410	99,928	1.024
B	1,950	40,000	1.049
C	2,800	43,643	1.064
D	2,500	12,230	1.204
E	7,000	7,631	1.917

Example of index calculation for supplier A:

$$QCPI = \frac{SQ\ Cost + Purchased\ Cost}{Purchased\ Cost} = \frac{\$2,410 + \$99,928}{\$99,928} = 1.024$$

The company also developed a method of interpreting the quality cost performance index to assess each supplier. A perfect supplier would have no quality costs, since there would be no rejections or complaint investigations and receiving inspection would be unnecessary. Therefore, the index for a perfect supplier would be:

$$QCPI = \frac{SQ\ Cost + Purchased\ Cost}{Purchased\ Cost} = \frac{0 + Purchased\ cost}{Purchased\ Cost} = 1.000$$

The actual assessment used by this company was:

Index (QCPI)	Interpretation
1.000–1.009	Excellent
1.010–1.039	Good
1.040–1.069	Fair
1.070–1.099	Poor
1.100+	Immediate corrective action required

Using this assessment, first priority for this company is to obtain immediate corrective action for suppliers D and E indicated above.

Results for the overall program were encouraging, with the percentage of total suppliers rated good or better increasing from 75% to 80% and supplier quality costs reducing 8.5% in the first year.

Many variations and innovations can be developed for utilizing quality costs to evaluate supplier performance. How it is done is less important than the recognition of the size and impact of the supplier-related quality costs. Once recognized, planned steps can be developed for measuring, comparing, and analyzing so that improvement can be made.

A Return on Investment Analysis Using Supplier Quality Costs

The previously discussed firm also developed a return on investment and analysis strategy utilizing supplier quality costs. Supplier E had a quality cost performance index (QCPI) of 1.917. This was interpreted to require immediate corrective action on the part of the buyer company.

First thoughts centered on canceling the contract with supplier E and transferring the tools to either supplier A, B, or C, all of which had much better quality performance indices. A closer look at the situation revealed that suppliers A, B, or C may not do much better initially since this was a new product that was undergoing significant start-up expenses. A trip to supplier E revealed that, although the company did not have a staff of problem solvers, the quality system and manufacturing equipment of supplier E were adequate.

The buyer then considered the idea of sending a problem solver colleague to supplier E for two weeks to expedite the reduction of start-up difficulties. In making this decision, the buyer used the return on investment (ROI) concept:

$$ROI = \frac{Savings \times 100}{Investment}$$

Savings would be the reduction in supplier quality costs anticipated through this approach. In time, the purchased cost probably would be reduced as well. The investment for doing this would be the wages, fringe benefits, and travel expenses of the problem solver. For this situation, a potential reduction of $6,000 in quality costs was estimated for an investment of $1,500 to provide help to supplier E. The return on investment was:

$$ROI = \frac{\$6,000 \times 100}{\$1,500} = 400\%$$

Obviously, this is a good idea if the objectives can be achieved.

COST OF QUALITY IN SMALL BUSINESS

In this section we will use the results of research at four small firms to look at quality costs in the small business sector and provide recommendations for making a cost of quality study in a small manufacturing or service firm.

Representatives from four companies were interviewed to gather information regarding the cost of quality in small businesses. The companies included two manufacturing concerns and two from the service sector.

One of the manufacturing companies makes packaging for use in the food industry. Plastic film on rolls is bonded together to form bags, and these go through a rolling process in which the customer's logo is printed on the outside of the bag. The product is then cut to the specified size. The company employs from 100 to 249 employees and has annual sales between $20 and $50 million.

The second manufacturing company makes electrical surge protectors. The casings for the protectors are purchased from outside sources and the company makes and assembles the inner components. The firm employs from 100 to 200 employees and has annual sales between $2 and $8 million.

One of the service industries provides programming services and prepackaged software. This company is involved with software analysis and the design and development of database decision system software. It employs 90 to 110 employees and has annual sales of approximately $14 million.

The last company interviewed is a managed healthcare services company. The firm acts as an intermediary between insurance companies and the insured. It employs approximately 500 people and its annual revenues are between $25 and $50 million.

Results of the Study

A summary of the research results is presented in Table 4.1. For each of the four categories of the cost of quality (prevention, appraisal, and internal and external failure), the table specifies the elements of cost the companies reported as applicable (indicated by an X). The Yes/No notation refers to the capturing of data: "Yes" means that the firm currently records the data; "No" means that the data are not currently being recorded but could be.

Internal Failure Costs

In all of the companies interviewed, the element of rework was an applicable cost of quality and all are currently capturing this figure from basic data now recorded. Scrap was an issue for three of the four companies; one of the service companies is a hybrid, and scrap is tracked in manufacturing. It appears that in the service industries, scrap may not apply. All four companies answered "Yes" to the area of Failure Analysis, but none of them is currently capturing the dollar amount spent in this area (each indicated that this amount could be determined by converting time card data to dollars). No pattern was observed across firms with respect to the supplier area or 100% sorting (two of the companies indicated that this applied, two indicated that it did not). The manufacturing companies indicated that they do lower prices because of a product downgrade and are able to capture this amount; this area did not apply to the service firms.

Table 4.1 Summary of categories.

Category/Element	Manufacturing 1		Manufacturing 2		Service 1		Service 2	
Internal Failure								
1. Scrap	X	Yes	X	Yes	X	Yes	N/A	
2. Rework	X	Yes	X	Yes	X	Yes	X	Yes
3. Analysis	X	No	X	No	X	No	X	No
4. Supplier	X	Yes	N/A		X	No	X	No
5. Sorting	N/A		X	No	N/A		X	No
6. Downgrading	X	Yes	X	Yes	N/A		N/A	
External Failure								
1. Warranty	N/A		X	No	X	No	N/A	
2. Complaint adj.	X	No	X	No	X	No	X	No
3. Ret. material	X	Yes	X	Yes	N/A		N/A	
4. Allowances	X	Yes	X	Yes	X	No	X	No
Appraisal								
1. Incoming	X	No	X	No	X	No	X	No
2. In-process	X	No	X	No	X	No	X	No
3. Final	X	No	X	No	X	No	X	No
4. Quality audit	X	No	X	No	X	No	X	No
5. Equipment test	X	No	X	No	X	No	N/A	
6. Matls & service	N/A		X	No	X	No	N/A	
7. Inventory	N/A		X	No	N/A		N/A	
Prevention								
1. Quality plan	X	No	X	No	X	No	X	No
2. Products review	X	No	X	No	X	No	X	No
3. Process plan	X	No	X	No	N/A		N/A	
4. Quality audit	X	No	X	No	X	No	X	No
5. Supplier eval.	X	No	N/A		X	No	X	No
6. Training	N/A		X	No	N/A		X	No

X – Indicates element applies to company
Yes – Indicates data are currently captured
No – Indicates data are not currently captured but could be

External Failure Costs

One area applied to all companies, Complaint Adjustment. None of the firms is currently capturing costs in this area, but each company indicated that these charges could be captured. The methods for estimating complaint costs varied, but all are based on some method of determining or collecting the actual hours spent on the adjustment of complaints. Because the companies are small, most of the complaints are handled by middle or upper level management. These individuals indicated that their time allocation could be determined through better recordkeeping.

The other element that applies to all companies is Allowances. Each company indicated that concessions are made to customers when they accept substandard products. The manufacturing companies are capturing these costs using data that are currently being recorded. The service companies, however, are not currently capturing these costs. Both service companies indicated that these costs could be determined using current data (either penalties charged by the customer or the amount of fees waived because of the problem encountered).

Appraisal Costs

Incoming, In-Process, Final Inspection and Testing, and Product Quality Audits apply to all of the companies surveyed. However, none of the companies is currently capturing these costs. All companies indicated that these costs could be determined if their labor reporting were more specific (that is, if time cards were used for each individual action performed by employees). This is a pervasive theme throughout this analysis; the use of more definitive labor reporting would allow most of the costs of quality to be captured and dollarized. None of the other areas of Appraisal applies to all of the companies interviewed nor is there any pattern such as "Yes" for manufacturing and "No" for service.

Prevention Costs

The areas that apply to all four companies are Quality Planning, New Products Review, and Quality Audit. All companies indicated that these costs are not currently being captured but could be. Once again, the overriding factor seems to be that more efficient use of time cards would serve as a means of determining costs in these areas. No pattern is evident in the other areas in this category.

Overview

Two themes seem to be found in all four companies. First, since the firms are small, a great many quality problems are handled by management, often without understanding the extra costs incurred throughout the honeycomb of the firm. Each company indicated in its own way that the costs of correcting problems could be captured if the individuals involved would keep records of the costs incurred in solving problems and pacifying customers.

The other area pervasive across companies is that the costs of quality that apply but are not being captured could be captured or estimated through the use of some sort of time capturing device (time cards indicating the amount of time spent on specific areas of inspection, testing, and so on). Because the companies are small, management is able to talk out problems with one another. The time spent solving problems is also a cost of quality. This cost could also be estimated from meeting minutes, better record keeping on the part of the individuals involved, and so on.

The Impact of Quality on Sales Revenue

Traditionally the measurement of the cost of quality focuses on the costs of nonconformities, of defects or errors in the goods or services delivered to external or internal customers (external and internal failure costs). An important cost that is not usually measured is lost sales due to poor quality. This is referred to as a hidden cost (see discussion in Chapter 1) because it has not been measured. These lost sales are due to customer dissatisfaction with the goods or services provided. This dissatisfaction may result in a loss of current customers—"customer defections"—and an inability to attract new customers because of a tarnished quality reputation. This loss is difficult to measure although, if sufficient market research information is available, it can sometimes be used with other information to estimate the loss of sales revenue due to poor quality. In any event, the impact of quality on sales revenue should be considered, at least by identifying the areas of customer dissatis-faction, and taking action to improve retention of current customers and create new ones.

Care needs to be taken that only clear cases of lost revenues are attributed to poor quality. If the sales area sees that missed sales can be attributed to operation's mistakes, a non-productive argument is set up within the company. If a specific customer reduces or cancels a specific quantity due to a documented quality issue, then that is a candidate for the loss of revenue in quality cost measures.

Recommendations for Making an Initial Study in a Small Firm

One approach follows these steps:

1. In monetary terms, introduce management to whatever data are available. This will show them how big the potential problem is in terms that will get their attention.

2. Propose that a committee be formed to gauge the cost of quality. Ideally, someone from management should chair this committee and it should include personnel from major line functions.

3. Adapt the elements comprising the costs of quality to fit the firm. This list can be prepared by a quality manager or a finance manager with inputs from accounting and other functions.

4. Have upper level management affirm the definitions and assign duties based on these definitions, including an agenda for data collection.

5. Collect, summarize, and analyze the data. The analysis should identify the "vital few" failure costs. Specific improvement projects should then be proposed to determine and remove the root causes.

6. Select one quality improvement project and pursue it using modern problem solving tools. Take this opportunity to learn and demonstrate the effectiveness of the problem solving tools.

7. Review the full study and select additional improvement projects to pursue.

This approach provides an opportunity for upper management to demonstrate leadership on quality, and it also assures the involvement of functional areas so that the study receives priority and the results are recognized as credible. In defining the costs of quality, keep these points in mind:

1. Customize the definition for your own organization. The failure, appraisal, and prevention categories presented here have proven useful in practice. As a possible starting point, use that framework along with the elements reported in Table 4.1 for a manufacturing or a service firm. Review Appendix B for additional elements that may apply to your organization. Create a draft of the definition of categories, show it to various functions, and ask their input on additional elements or changes in wording. What results from all this is the "right" definition for your firm. Whether this definition conforms to the literature is not critical.

2. Obtain agreement of the executive management team on the elements of cost to be included before any data are collected. It's possible that summarized data on one or two key elements such as scrap and rework will gain management attention and generate approval for a full study. Ask the accountant to review this paper and other literature and prepare a draft of a definition of elements. The executive team could then review and discuss the draft and finalize the definition.

3. Don't limit the definition to only costs that directly involve the goods or services sold to customers (scrap, rework, complaints). Poor quality is now viewed as applying to any activity in the company. Any work that must be discarded or reprocessed should be viewed as a failure cost of quality. Thus when information is missing from a document, the time spent in retrieving the missing information contributes to the cost of quality.

4. Don't accept as inevitable camouflaged costs that are routinely incurred but are really part of the cost of quality. In manufacturing, examples include the cost of redesigning a product because it fails to meet customer needs or the cost of changing processes that are unable to meet product specifications. In the service sector, watch for activities that are described using words such as rework, check, expedite, correct, adjustment, and shrinkage.

Focus on the internal and external failure cost categories because these provide major opportunity for the removal of causes of customer dissatisfaction and reduction in costs of quality. These costs should be attacked first because "that's where the money is." Determining root causes and removing them will require some level of diagnosis, but the investment of time and resources can achieve a benefit-to-cost ratio ranging from 5-to-1 to as much as 10-to-1.

Appraisal costs are another area for potential reduction, but not until the causes of failure costs have been identified and removed, thereby reducing the need for appraisal. In the initial study, cost data are collected from different sources:

1. *Established accounts.* Examples are scrap or rework accounts that quantify costs incurred in these areas and price reductions driven by product downgrades.

2. *Analysis of ingredients of established accounts.* Make sure that only the costs of quality are included in the analysis. For example, customer returns will probably include returns for reasons other than product defects. These should not be quantified in the analysis. It may be necessary to view the source documents to determine the reason for a return.

3. *Basic accounting documents.* Inspection costs incurred in the operations area could be quantified by obtaining the names and the associated payroll data of the employees responsible.

4. *Estimates.* Several approaches may be needed:

   a. Temporary records. Some production workers spend part of their time repairing defective product. Timekeeping devices could be used to establish temporary records to capture costs incurred to repair defective products. These could help to estimate total repair costs.

   b. Work sampling. This random sampling approach determines the percentage of time spent in each of a number of predefined tasks. This percentage could then lead to an estimate of the costs incurred in these areas.

   c. Allocation of total resources. In the shipping department, part of an employee's time is spent on inspecting before packaging the product. There may be no provision for capturing this cost. To quantify this time and cost, ask each employee to estimate time spent on inspection while packaging the product.

   d. Unit cost data. Determine the cost of correcting a single error and then multiplied that number by the estimated number of errors of the same type that are expected per year. Examples include billing errors and scrap.

Reporting the Cost of Quality

Reporting the cost of quality can take three forms:

1. Special reports to support activities on quality improvement projects

2. Periodic reports to summarize current status on selected elements of the cost of quality

3. Comprehensive reports similar to the initial study described earlier

As structured quality improvement teams employing the project-by-project approach have emerged as a strong force, reporting on the cost of quality has focused on supporting activities for quality improvement projects. These reports should include information to help diagnose the problem, and information to track the change in costs as a problem solving remedy is implemented. What data are needed is determined by the team, and the team often collects its own data.

Although some companies have used a quality cost scoreboard to periodically give the status of key elements of the cost of quality, the trend is for the cost of quality and other quality related information to become integrated into the overall performance reporting system of organizations. A limited number of measures would be reported including the cost of quality.

Periodically (once or twice a year), a comprehensive report on the cost of quality is useful to summarize and consolidate the efforts and results of project teams and other quality improvement activities. Such a report should:

• Reflect the results of improvement efforts

• Provide guidance to identify major areas for future improvement efforts

Additionally, the report should be expressed in terms that are meaningful to management. The cost of quality can be related to several other measures. To determine what measures might be used, see the section on Quality Cost Bases in Chapter 2.

The comparative base used will determine the effect the results of the study will have on the attitude of management. The executives interviewed thought that costs as a percent of sales revenue, as a percent of profit, and as dollars per unit of product produced were meaningful measures.

Conclusions for Small Firms

Several promising conclusions emerge from this research.

First, small firms can estimate the cost of quality more easily than large firms. Fewer personnel and fewer lines of communication in small firms make it easier to trace and determine costs of events that lead to poor quality.

Second, analyzing the components of the cost of quality spotlights where most of this loss exists, defining the areas where improvement efforts should be focused to improve quality and reduce the extra costs of poor quality.

Finally, addressing the major contributors to the cost of quality by finding and eliminating the root causes is a golden opportunity for a firm to provide customers with better value. All firms claim these days to have products with the "best value," but this claim can be made tangible by using the savings in cost of quality (achieved by a quality improvement effort) to:

1. Finance additional product features without raising prices, or

2. Lower prices for products with existing features.

Either route to increased value will lead to higher sales income for the firm.

For many firms, estimating the cost of quality can be the catalyst to fuel action-oriented steps to achieve quality improvement.

SOFTWARE QUALITY COSTS

Software is significant in that it is both a product and a means of delivering a product or service. Software delivers the most important product, namely information. Software captures and connects information to link customers to products and services and localities to global resources. Software also acts as a control mechanism for systems, transactions, individual projects, and enterprise-wide activities.

Software consists of the computer programs, associated procedures, documentation, and data pertaining to the operation of a computer system. As a purely intellectual product, it is among the most labor-intensive, complex, and error-prone technologies in human history. Differentiated from the hardware, the physical machines on which software works, there are many types of software products and systems in the world today. These are often characterized either by business domains (for example, information systems) or by relationship to other software layered between the user and the computing machinery (for example, programs embedded in microprocessors to create intelligent devices and appliances).

The Development and Economics of Software

To highlight its distinctive characteristics, it is helpful to contrast the development or engineering of software with that of manufactured products.

- Software does not consist of physical components, so it does not align with the Weibull "bathtub" curve. Software does not "wear out"; its obsolescence is reflected in the currency of its design and its interaction with other software.

- Software is predominantly a customized creation, which is not replicated but enhanced or optimized with successive versions.

- Software is an intellectual, rather than a physical, product; its development is subject to human and logical constraints rather than physical laws.

- One cannot assume that a software specification is stable. Changing of requirements is expected behavior in software development.

- Productivity levels vary widely (more so in individuals than in teams).

- Product defects are the result of poor information, limited information, human misunderstandings, and human mistakes but not deficient materials.

- Manufactured goods are valued for their features; software is valued for its interactive functionality and nonfunctional attributes.

- The economics of software quality hinges on the process of understanding requirements.

- This process, more so than conformance, is commonly responsible for the value of a software product.

- The costs of the manufacturing phase of software production are insignificant. The bulk of software development costs are in the requirements elicitation and specification, design, implementation, and testing disciplines.

- Statistics cannot be applied to replications because software products are usually one of a kind.

- The cost of ownership is accounted differently because software assets are not capitalized and depreciated.

What is Software Quality?

Although there is no single comprehensive and complete standard definition of software quality, descriptions and terms are found in sources such as consensus national and international standards (ISO/IEC 9126, ISO/IEC 90003, IEEE Software Engineering Standards) and various books on the subject (Figure 4.1).

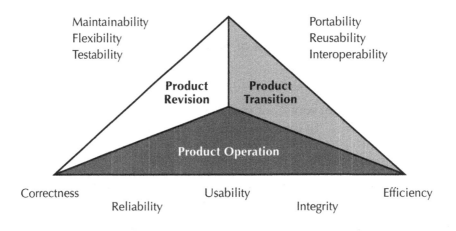

Figure 4.1   Software quality attributes.

ISO/IEC 9126 is a standard that identifies and captures quality attributes for computer software. It defines the major software quality attributes, distinguishing these as functionality, reliability, usability, efficiency, maintainability, and portability (Figure 4.2).

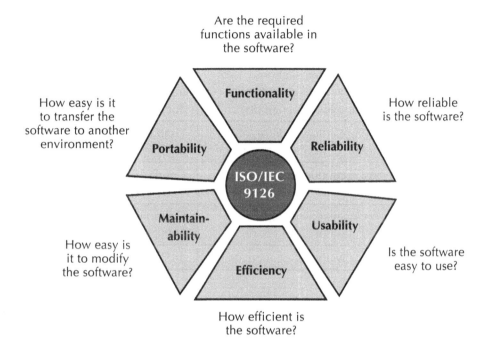

Figure 4.2   ISO/IEC 9126 software quality attributes.

Since software is used to support, enable, or automate professional services, it is reasonable to apply the service quality models when evaluating the value and effectiveness of a software solution when used in a service context (Table 4.2).

Table 4.2 Service quality model applied to software.

Service Quality Dimension	Examples	Relevance to Software
Image, expectations	Appropriate to software use, alignment to service model	Product "look and feel," replication of subject matter expertise
Reliability	Complete transactions, fulfillment of commitments, success on first attempts,	Confirmation numbers after transactions, traceability path, audit records, logs
Responsiveness	Prompt completion of steps, online or available assistance	Usability, online help, frequently asked questions (FAQ) section
Assurance	Instill confidence, make software users feel safe	Certification, security
Empathy	Personalized customer care, retention of customer details	Customization, independent configuration,
Tangibles	Visually appealing, convenient	24/7 uptime and availability

To summarize, it is important to reinforce the basic principles. The following are definitions of software quality from several high-level traditional quality perspectives:

- *Level of satisfaction.* The degree to which a customer or user perceives that a software product meets his or her composite needs and expectations

- *Product value.* The value of a software product relative to its various stakeholders and the competition

- *Key attributes.* The extent to which a software product possesses a desired combination of properties

- *Freedom from defects.* The degree to which a software product works correctly in target user environments, free from operational flaws

- *Process quality.* In relation to the development process by which the product is produced, the extent to which people do the right things in an effective way

Why is the Cost of Software Quality (CoSQ) Important Now?

If improving business success through software quality is a corporate goal (Figure 4.3), then we need answers to a few simple questions that are not often asked in today's software development situations. These questions are:

- How much does software quality cost?
- What are the benefits of good quality software?
- How good is our software quality?

Once the answers to these questions are known:

- Quality costs can be compared to overall software production costs and software product sales.
- Quality costs can be compared to benchmarks and norms.
- Deeper analysis can lead to actions to improve the competitive situation.
- The bottom line effect of improvement actions can be measured.
- The economic tradeoffs involved with software quality become visible, thus leading to better decision making.

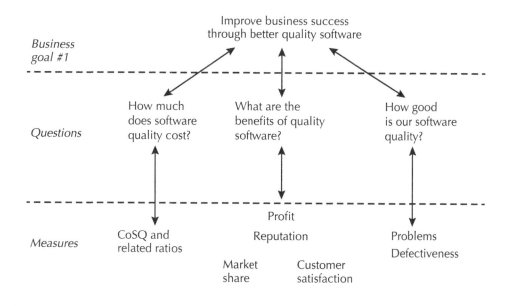

Figure 4.3   Cost of software quality (CoSQ) in context.

Applying Cost of Quality Principles to Software

Table 4.3 lists the four categories typical when applying costs of software quality. Most prevention costs are in the development cycle, except for organization-wide costs such as process definition and metrics collection and analysis.

Table 4.3   Typical costs of quality for software.

Cost Area		Description	Typical costs
Cost of control or conformance	Prevention costs	Defect avoidance; quality basis definition; project and process-oriented interventions	Efforts to define quality and set quality goals, standards, and thresholds; quality trade-off analysis; definition of release criteria for acceptance testing and related quality standards; training; process metric creation and planning; formal inspection
	Appraisal costs	Defect detection; discovery of product non-conformance; finding the level of non-conformance	Quality control gating processes, contract or proposal reviews, quality audits, go–no go decisions, quality assurance of subcontractors, inspections, static/dynamic analysis, testing, walk-through, desk-checking
Cost of failure of control or non-conformance	Internal failure costs	Pre-release defect or anomaly correction prior to delivery to the customer	Recode, retest, re-review, re-document, requirements rework, design rework
	External failure costs	Post-release defect or anomaly correction and related costs after delivery to the customer	Warranty support, resolution of complaints, reimbursement damage paid to customer, domino effect on other projects, damage to reputation or enterprise, added marketing to correct reputation problems, penalties

Cost of Software Quality and CMMI

Capability Maturity Model Integration® (CMMI) is a process improvement approach developed by the Software Engineering Institute (see www.sei.cmu. edu/cmmi). Originally developed as the Capability Maturity Model for Software, the full set of industry best practices now includes CMMI models specific to acquisition, development, and services.

Key practices include causal analysis, configuration management, data collection, project management, quality assurance, requirements engineering, risk management, and verification and validation. Implementation of these practices has led to demonstrable organizational improvements in many measures of performance such as schedule and cost predictability, product and service quality, productivity, customer satisfaction, and return on investment.

The basic CMMI framework is built around the idea of levels of maturity, each of which can be obtained only after successfully implementing all key practices of the previous level. The five-level model (Figure 4.4) represents a roadmap for targeting and sustaining a process improvement initiative, with each increase in maturity level typically requiring as much as two or more years of concerted effort.

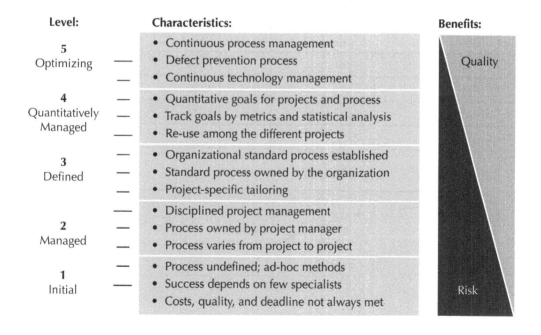

Figure 4.4   Basic CMMI framework.

There has been longstanding speculation about the nature and extent of reductions in quality costs resulting from organizational maturity improvements (Knox, 1993).[3] Knox developed a theoretical model for the cost of software quality (Figure 4.5).Other studies of quality improvement (Jones 2011) have reported a variety of measures without allowing direct calculation of cost-of-quality categories. For example, Table 4.4 shows defect injection and removal rates. (The economics are obscured because what Jones calls "efficiency" values are actually "effectiveness" percentages, and thus without cost considerations.)

A few reported case studies, however, have confirmed suspicions about quality cost benefits from such process improvements. The classic first sets of data were reported in the early and mid-1990s from Raytheon Electronics Systems Group (RES) (Dion 1993,[4] Haley 1996).[5]

Table 4.4 Software quality and the SEI Capability Maturity Model (CMMI) for projects of 5,000 function points in size.

CMMI level	Defect potential per function point	Defect removal efficiency	Delivered defects per function point
SEI CMMI 1	5.50	73%	1.49
SEI CMMI 2	4.00	90%	0.40
SEI CMMI 3	3.00	95%	0.15
SEI CMMI 4	2.50	97%	0.08
SEI CMMI 5	2.25	98%	0.05

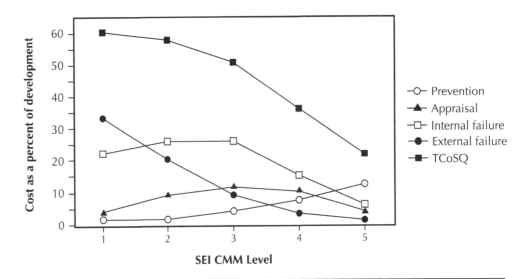

Figure 4.5 Knox's theoretical model for cost of software quality.

Starting at CMMI Level 1, RES introduced a software process improvement program in August 1988. Using the results of tracking 15 projects, they achieved CMMI Level 3 practices in a little over three years (see Figure 4.6).

In the Level 1 stage, RES's total CoSQ fluctuated between 55% and 67% of total project costs, and by the time it reached Level 3 process maturity, their total CoSQ had dropped to approximately 40%. By 1996, this organization's total CoSQ was approximately 15% of total project costs and the rework due to both internal and external nonconformances had been reduced to less than 5%. (For a more extensive discussion of CoSQ at RES, see CoSQ case study on page 184.)

A third source of CoSQ data is a Price Waterhouse study[6] that analyzed the costs and benefits of software quality standards from a survey of 19 United Kingdom (UK) software suppliers.[7] The study estimated the cost of conformance (prevention and appraisal costs) to be 23% to 34% of development effort. The study also estimated nonconformance (failure) costs at 15% of development effort for a total CoSQ of 38% to 49% of development effort. It must be noted that this study excluded the costs of unit testing and rework because the suppliers could not separate these costs. With increases in the estimates to account for this exclusion, CoSQ in a software organization with a quality system can range from 40% to 55% of development costs, with a conformance costs-to-nonconformance costs ratio ranging from 1.5 to 2.

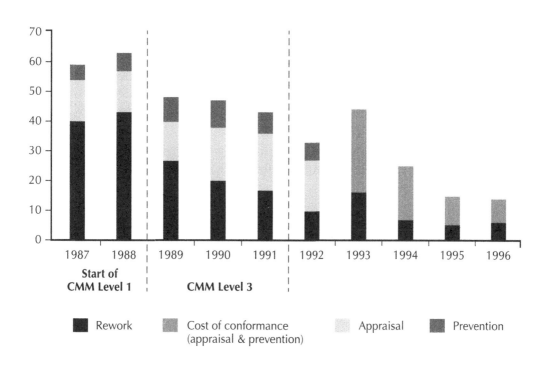

Figure 4.6   Cost of software quality for 15 projects at RES.

As compared to the RES graph, these figures generally agree with a period late in 1990 when RES was approaching CMMI Level 3: RES's CoSQ was about 45% of development, and its ratio of conformance to nonconformance costs was about 2.0 (conformance~30/nonconformance~15).

Based on the data in Figure 4.6, we can expect CoSQ, with the present state of software engineering practice, to range from 20% to 70% of development costs. Even accounting for the margin between production costs and sales, CoSQ appears to be roughly twice manufacturing CoQ.

More recently, Diane Gibson and Dennis Goldenson have cataloged measured decreases in internal failure costs for maturity levels[8] 1 through 4 (see Table 4.5).

The same report also related that an anonymous Raytheon level 3 site had reduced its costs of rework by 42% over several years. Similarly, a Siemens Information Systems organization reduced cost of poor quality from over 45% to under 30% over a three-year period as they moved toward level 5.

In an article published in 2007, A. Q. Liu shared results[9] from 191 projects conducted as the Motorola Software Group China Center upgraded to CMMI from 2000 to 2006. Due to improved appraisal processes, particularly product peer review and software test processes, the organization was able to reduce its overall cost of quality by more than one third from its pre-CMMI baseline and noted that the "cost of poor quality" (presumably failure costs) remained at less than 5% during the same period.

Potential Benefits of Using CoSQ

The work at RES demonstrates one of the benefits of measuring and using CoSQ, justification for quality initiatives. Examples of return on investment (ROI) in quality improvement initiatives speak most clearly to managers responsible for maintaining a profitable organization. However, CoSQ can be used for a number of other benefits. It can:

- Provide cost data for motivational purposes by demonstrating the relationship of employee efforts to the bottom line

- Provide a basis for budgeting the quality operation

Table 4.5   CMMI level rework as percentage of total project costs.

Level	Percentage
1	41
2	18
3	11
4	6

- Compare and identify the most cost-effective process improvements
- Provide a measure for comparing the success of projects
- Identify quality improvement candidates

Elements of a CoSQ Effort

The overall process of measuring and using cost of quality information specifically for software process improvement is shown in Figure 4.7. One key input to the process is definition of a project work breakdown structure (WBS). The total process involves gathering data from sources in accounting and quality. Subsequent steps may include collection of data from new quality metrics, data analysis, and presentation of results.

Accounting. Getting quality cost data assumes that costs have been accounted for using task and expense elements that can be summed into the four major categories of quality costs. Many software organizations track costs in a manner amenable to quality costing, but many others do not. In the latter case, a preliminary step of defining and installing such a chart of accounts is required. A sample of such a chart of quality costs is provided in Table 4.6. The quality elements in a software organization's chart of accounts must be tailored to reflect its software process. To realize the full benefit of CoSQ, it must also allow for the addition of process improvement tasks.

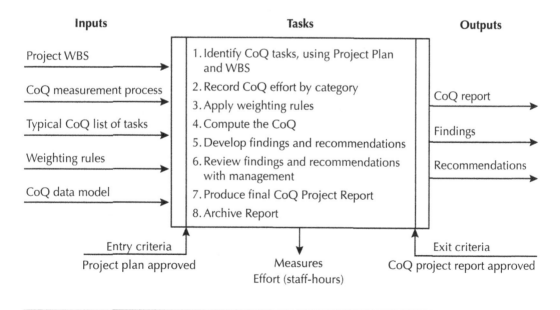

Figure 4.7 Top level modified ETVX description of the process to measure the CoSQ.

In best cases, quality costs can be taken directly from departmental accounting reports. In other cases, it may be necessary to resort to basic accounting and engineering records such as schedules, time reports, defect reports, and purchasing records. In worst cases, one may fall back on interviews with members of the software organization in order to construct estimates of each quality cost element. A controlled scientific study is unlikely, and incomplete data can suffice in beginning a software cost benefit analysis. With time and greater understanding, incomplete data can be filled in.

One of the pitfalls of a CoSQ program has to do with "controversial cost elements." Usually the question is about which costs are normal operating costs and which are quality costs. An example would be the cost of producing a project management plan. Although this plan is produced for the sake of managing a project's expenses and schedule, it also influences product and process quality. It is helpful to keep in mind the following points:

- Arguments over controversial elements have been known to sabotage cost of quality programs.

- The largest quality costs are those that are most easily discerned (reviews, software quality assurance, testing, and rework). Therefore, it is often safe to exclude controversial elements without unduly affecting the total CoSQ.

- Consistency throughout a CoSQ program is more important than thorough inclusion of quality costs because consistency allows for clear identification of improvements as well as candidates for improvement.

Concerns may also arise as to how quality costs should be categorized. Again, consistency is important. For example, in Table 4.7 the costs associated with formal inspections (peer reviews) are treated as prevention costs rather than as appraisal costs. This is a matter of interpretation, depending on when a work product is considered ready for appraisal. In manufacturing, inspections are conducted on pieces after they are produced; in software production, inspections may be incorporated into the production process per the peer review key process area for the SEI CMMI Level 3. For documentation, this means that a document is not complete until it has undergone a peer review and has been revised. The same is true for code, especially when code inspections precede unit testing; clearly an appraisal activity.

Quality Metrics Collection. The CoQ has been used primarily in a fundamental approach to quality, that is focusing on defect rates (manufacturing) or service problem reports (service industries) rather than broader approaches that would take into account factors such as usability, testability, maintainability, and so forth. The fundamental approach has the advantages of straightforward measurement and ease of understanding. It also allows comparison of dissimilar products. Most software producers take a fundamental approach to quality. (See Figures 4.8 and 4.9, and Table 4.6 for examples.)

Project charge codes

Codes for charging time to project activities are 10 characters: TTPPPPANNQ

TT	=	Two characters for process type, for example SW for software
PPPP	=	Four characters that designate a project
ANN	=	Three characters that designate the activity in the WBS, such as A01
Q	=	One character that designates the category relative to quality costs.

The value of Q is one of the following:

D	Initial development of work products
P	Defect prevention activities
T	Initial test of work product
R	Product rework
M	Miscellaneous/other

Software WBS activities/CoSQ modifiers

The following chart indicates what types of categories with regard to quality costs may be used for each WBS activity. For example, in requirements development, initial development of requirements document would be D, validation of requirements with a customer would be P, reworking a requirements with a customer would be P, and reworking a requirements document would be R.

		D	P	T	R	M
A01	Project management planning					•
A02	Requirements development/validation	•	•		•	
A03	Product concept development	•	•		•	
A04	Requirements analysis	•	•		•	
A05	Functional concept development	•	•		•	
A06	Define architecture	•	•		•	
A07	Test-plan development			•	•	
A08	Software configuration management (SCM) planning					•
A09	Detailed functional specification	•	•		•	
A10	Detailed design, code, debug	•	•		•	
A11	Unit testing			•	•	
A12	Integration testing			•	•	
A13	System test scripts			•	•	
A14	System test specification			•	•	
A15	User information development	•	•		•	
A16	User evaluation		•			
A17	Final test			•	•	
A18	Beta test			•	•	
A19	Project plan maintenance and updates					•
A20	Project tracking and metrics					•
A21	Software quality assurance		•			
A22	Subcontract management					•
A23	SCM builds	•	•		•	
	Other SCM functions					•
A24	Requirements and change management					•
A25	Establish/maintain development environment					•
A26	Miscellaneous activities					•

Figure 4.8 A software project charge scheme using an activity-based WBS with CoSQ modifiers.

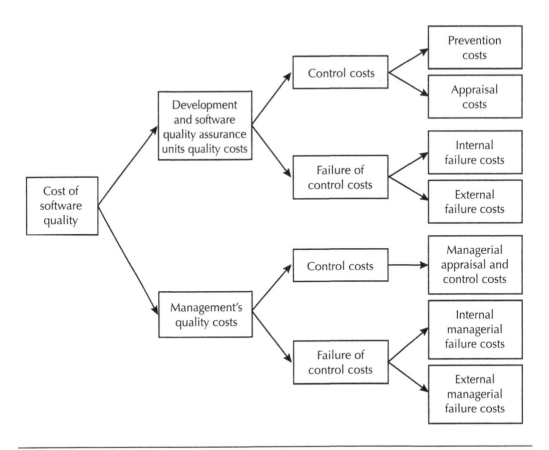

Figure 4.9 The proposed inclusive CoSQ model — targeted at software development projects.

Table 4.6   Typical cost items according to the proposed CoSQ model (examples).

Body in the organization responsible for quality cost	Class of costs of software quality	Typical quality cost items for each subclass
Software development and SQA teams	Control costs	Prevention costs: • Investments in development of and updating of procedures and work instructions • Investments in development and regular operation costs of software configuration management system • Investments in development and regular operation of software quality metrics • Instruction of new employees in those SQA subjects and procedures required by their position • Certification of employees for positions that require special certification • Internal and external quality audit
		Appraisal costs: • Performance of various reviews • Performance of unit, integration, and software system tests • Quality assurance of subcontractors and other external participants
Software development teams	Failure of control costs	Internal failure costs: • Redesign or corrections subsequent to design review and test findings • Reprogramming or correcting programs in response to test findings • Repeated design review and retesting (regression tests)
		External failure costs: • Resolution of customer complaints during the warranty period • Correction of software defects detected during regular operation • Damages paid to customer in case of a severe software failure • Reimbursement of customer's purchase costs, in case of total dissatisfaction • Insurance premium against customer damage claims in case of severe software failure • Hidden external failure costs, that is, reduction of sales as a result of damaged reputation, increased investments in sales promotion under-pricing of tender bidding to counter the effects of past software external failures

(continued)

Table 4.6 Typical cost items according to the proposed CoSQ model (examples). *(continued)*

Body in the organization responsible for quality cost	Class of costs of software quality	Typical quality cost items for each subclass
Management	Control costs	Managerial appraisal and control costs • Costs of conduct of contract reviews • Costs for preparation of project and quality plans and their periodic updating • Costs for performance of regular progress control
	Failure of control costs	Internal managerial failure costs: • Unplanned development costs resulting from underestimation of resources for submitted proposals • *Domino effect:* Damages to other projects planned to be performed by team members involved in delayed projects due to extra costs for recruitment of replacement team members*
	Failure of control costs	External managerial failure costs: • Damages paid to customer as compensation for late project completion resulting from an unrealistic schedule presented in proposal • Damages paid to customer as compensation for late project completion resulting from failure to recruit sufficient and appropriate team members • *Domino effect:* Damages for delayed completion paid to clients of other projects planned to be performed by team members involved in delayed projects* • Hidden external failure costs, that is, reduction of sales as a result of damaged reputation, increased investments in sales promotion under-pricing of tender bidding to counter the effects of significant past delayed completion of projects due to managerial failures in appraisal and/or progress control tasks

Note: * These damages should be considered managerial failure costs belonging to the original project, whose scheduling problems interfered with the progress of other projects. Should they materialize, one can expect the domino effect to obstruct the progress of several other projects and induce considerable hidden external failure costs.

Software metrics are used to make timely, data-driven decisions, track progress, and evaluate the impact of changes to products, processes, and resources. Because software is not tangible, metrics can be either predicted or calculated and often represent subjective impressions as objective ordinal values. Metrics are effective when linked to goals and objectives, and they serve as evidence responding to the "questions" surrounding the completion of particular goals. For example, if an organization has an explicit goal of having no open critical defects on release, an appropriate metric used to evaluate goal fulfillment would be the quantity of open critical defects relative to total defects at a particular development milestone (beta test milestone).

A system for collecting both defect metrics and the failure portion of quality costs would provide data having the added advantage of aiding in root cause analysis and of identifying the most costly defects (see discussion in Chapter 1).

In order to avoid reporting contradictory or irrelevant comparisons between the different types of software and programming methods (for example, comparing nuclear-based medical software with a telephone gaming app), the total cost of ownership (TCO) is a good place to start for measuring CoSQ improvements.

TCO permits the cost of quality initiatives to link back to Lean and Agile methods for software development and make use of a value stream in software engineering to distinguish value-added activities (that is, development based on approved requirements) from non value-added activities (for example, finding and fixing defects, realignment of misconfigured or incorrectly labeled modules or components). Examples of wastes that would inflate TCO without adding value include:

- Rework to address missing, incorrect, or extra code

- Unassigned development backlog waiting for ownership

- Excessive features of low or negligible value

- Unused documentation

- Concurrent assignments or frequent switching

- Handover between resources

- Delays for approvals, decisions, and resources (for example, waiting for "code complete" before beginning quality assurance activities)

Table 4.7   Sample CoSQ chart.

1	**Prevention Costs**	

1.1	Requirements	
	1.1.1	Marketing research for customer/user quality needs
	1.1.2	Customer/user quality surveys
	1.1.3	Product quality risk analysis
	1.1.4	Prototyping for customer review
	1.1.5	User requirements/specification reviews/inspections
1.2	Project	
	1.2.1	Project quality planning
	1.2.2	Project process validation
	1.2.3	Quality assessment of development platform and tools
	1.2.4	Platform and tools development for quality
	1.2.5	Developer quality training
	1.2.6	Quality metrics data collection
	1.2.7	Design for quality: software component reuse
	1.2.8	Formal inspections / peer reviews
	1.2.9	Project configuration management
	1.2.10	Project change management
	1.2.11	Supplier capability assessment
1.3	Reuse library	
	1.3.1	Salaries
	1.3.2	Expenses
	1.3.3	Training
	1.3.4	Platform and tools
1.4	Configuration management administration	
	1.4.1	Salaries
	1.4.2	Expenses
	1.4.3	Training
	1.4.4	Platform and tools
1.5	SQA administration	
	1.5.1	SQA salaries
	1.5.2	SQA expenses
	1.5.3	Software process and standards definition and publication
	1.5.4	Metrology: data maintenance, analysis, and reporting
	1.5.5	SQA program planning
	1.5.6	SQA performance reporting
	1.5.7	SQA education/training
	1.5.8	Process improvement
	1.5.9	SQA process compliance audits

(continued)

Table 4.7   Sample CoSQ chart.   *(continued)*

2 Appraisal Costs

2.1	Supplied product testing
2.2	Project appraisal costs
2.2.1	Verification and validation activities
2.2.2	Testing: planning, platforms, setup, test data generation, test execution and logging, reporting, test data evaluation
2.2.3	Product quality audits
2.3	External appraisals
2.3.1	Process maturity evaluation
2.3.2	Field performance trials
2.3.3	Special product evaluations

3 Internal Failure Costs

3.1	Product design defect costs
3.1.1	Causal analysis and reporting
3.1.2	Design corrective action
3.1.3	Rework and retest due to design corrective action
3.1.4	Work products wasted due to design changes
3.2	Purchased product defect cost
3.2.1	Defect analysis cost
3.2.2	Cost of obtaining product fix
3.2.3	Cost of defect work-arounds
3.2.4	Rework
3.3	Implementation defect costs
3.3.1	Defect measurement and reporting
3.3.2	Defect fixing
3.3.3	Causal analysis and reporting
3.3.4	Project process corrective action
3.3.5	Fix inspection
3.3.6	Retest and integration

4 External Failure Costs

4.1	Technical support for responding to defect complaints
4.2	Product returned due to defect
4.3	Maintenance and release due to defects
4.4	Defect notification costs
4.5	Upgrade due to defect
4.6	Service agreement claims (warranty expense reports)
4.7	Litigation costs and liability claims (insurance and legal reports)
4.8	Penalties (product contract reports)
4.9	Costs to maintain customer/user goodwill due to dissatisfaction (sales reports)
4.10	Lost sales/market share due to quality problems (field salesperson reports)

Sources of quality cost data: Ordinarily, quality cost data for the majority of categories would be obtained from salary and expense reports. Exceptions in the external failure category are shown here in parentheses.

Table 4.8 Cost of software quality data.

	Site A American Engineers (19)	Site A American Managers (5)	Site B European Engineers (13)	Site C European Engineers (14)	Site D European Engineers (9)	Course A 2008 (8)	Course B 2008 (14)	Course C 2009 (11)	Course D 2010 (8)	Course E 2011 (15)	Course F 2012 (10)
Cost of performance	41%	44%	34%	31%	34%	29%	43%	45%	45%	34%	40%
Cost of rework	30%	26%	23%	41%	34%	28%	29%	30%	25%	32%	31%
Cost of appraisal	18%	14%	32%	21%	26%	24%	18%	14%	20%	27%	20%
Cost of prevention	11%	16%	11%	8%	7%	14%	10%	11%	10%	8%	9%
Quality defects per 1000 lines of code	71	8	23	35	17	403	19	48	35	60	55

CoSQ Analysis and Dynamics. Plotting CoSQ against a quality measure (such as total cost of ownership or product defects) provides the CoSQ curve and, plotted against time, reveals trends in an organization's quality processes. This addresses most of the goals of quality costing: justification, motivation, budgeting, and process improvement cost effectiveness. Pareto analysis, based on the principle that quality costs are localized (80% of quality costs are incurred by 20% of the quality nonconformances), can be used to identify candidates for process improvement (see Chapter 5). When CoSQ is categorized by product and process sources, typically one or two sources will be shown to incur much higher costs than the others.

In analyzing CoSQ data, the dynamics of the model must be taken into account. The following are some of the factors that affect CoSQ over time:

- Advances in software technology, for example the prevalence of graphical user interfaces, create new demands on software producers.

- Growing user sophistication creates demands for increased functionality and better support (documentation, training, technical services).

- Better applications and systems set new standards for performance and reliability.

- Better software production technology, for example in testing and configuration management, supports higher quality goals.

- Reduced cycle time and time to market increase competition in the marketplace and may be accompanied by changes in actual or perceived quality.

These factors may have the effect of shifting the point of diminishing returns over time, usually to the right. For example, either better software production technology or growing user sophistication can effect a shift in the optimum CoSQ toward a higher level of quality.

CoSQ presentation. Relationships that have the greatest impact on management are:

- Quality costs relative to the total cost of ownership for software

- Quality costs as a percent of sales

- Quality costs compared to profit

- Quality costs compared to the magnitude of the current problem

In addition to these, showing CoSQ as a percent of total development costs is appropriate to software for several reasons. First, sales and profit may not have a direct relationship to the actual cost of a software product since software pricing is often dictated by market forces. Second, all but a small percentage of software development costs can be measured in labor hours, so the costs can be readily shown in either hours or dollars. Third, the state of the art in software development is such that comparing quality costs to development costs illustrates the magnitude of the current challenge.

Conclusions

CoQ is a proven technique in manufacturing and service industries, both for communicating the value of quality initiatives and for identifying quality initiative candidates. CoSQ offers the same promise for the software industry, but could be used more. Initial uses of CoSQ indicate that it represents a very large percentage of development costs—60% and higher for organizations that are unaware of improvement opportunities. CoSQ use can, however, demonstrate significant cost savings—such as Raytheon's fourfold reduction in rework—for software organizations willing to undertake quality improvement initiatives. Perhaps more importantly, the use of CoSQ enables an understanding of the economic trade-offs that accompany activities and expenditures made for improving the quality of delivered software.

End Notes

1. Dale, B. G. and J. J. Plunkett, *Quality Costing,* 2nd edition, Chapman and Hall, London, 1995.

2. Schiffauerova, A. and V. Thomson, "Managing Cost of Quality: Insight into Industry Practice," *The TQM Magazine,* 2006.

3. Knox, S.T. "Modeling the Cost of Software Quality," *Digital Technical Journal,* 5(4), 9–16 (Fall 1993).

4. Dion, R. "Process Improvement and the Corporate Balance Sheet," *IEEE Software,* Vol. 10, No. 4, July 1993, pp. 28–35.

5. Haley, T.J. Software Process Improvement at Raytheon, *IEEE Software,* 13 (November), 33–41 (1996).

6. Price Waterhouse Management Consultants, *Software Quality Standards: The Costs and Benefits. A Review for the Department of Trade and Industry,* Price Waterhouse Management Consultants, London, 1988.

7. Gibson, Diane; Dennis Goldenson; and Keith Kost. Performance Results of CMMI-Based Process Improvement (CMU/SEI-2006-TR-004). Software Engineering Institute, Carnegie Mellon University, 2006. www.sei.cmu.edu/library/abstracts/reports/06tr004.cfm

8. Liu, A.Q. 2007. "Motorola Software Group's China Center: Value Added by CMMI." *Software Technology News.* 10,1, 19-23. www.journal.thedacs.com/issue/41/79

Chapter 5

Quality Improvement and
Reducing Quality Costs

This chapter is designed to provide guidance to company management and professionals engaged in quality program management. This guidance will enable them to structure and manage programs for quality cost reduction. It describes techniques for using quality costs analysis in programs to reduce overall costs and thereby improve profits.

Although most of the examples and discussions that follow relate to manufacturing industries, the techniques and methods described are just as applicable to the various service industries and may be used by management in banking, insurance, healthcare, retail, and so on.

Today, it is well proven that improving quality of work processes results in lower total quality costs. By total quality costs, we mean cost elements from marketing, design, purchasing, manufacturing, and service. Every part of the product cycle generates some quality costs. To avoid leaving savings behind, programs for identifying and improving cost must be comprehensive enough to involve all these functions.

THE QUALITY COST IMPROVEMENT PHILOSOPHY

It is a fact, too often unrecognized, that every dollar saved in the total cost of quality is directly translatable into a dollar of pretax earnings. It is also a fact that quality improvements and quality cost reductions cannot be created merely by declaration—they must be earned through the process of problem solving. The first step is the identification of problems, which we define as an area of high quality costs. Every problem identified as quality costs is an opportunity for profit improvement.

Here we discuss quality programs that are *not* confined to manufacturing. Most people recognize that quality is also affected by many factors outside of manufacturing, but many quality programs do not concern themselves with these factors. In some cases, quality program efforts have been attempts at not allowing things to get any worse (control) instead of striving to make things better (improvement). As a result, things have deteriorated in many places simply because controls are not, and never can be, 100% effective. Improving quality is similar to improving product costs. It is everybody's job and everybody is for the idea, but until there is management commitment to improve and a formal program for forcing improvement, it just doesn't happen.

This chapter describes what each company function must do to improve quality (that is, prevent defects), through involvement of people in marketing, design, purchasing, accounting, manufacturing, and quality assurance. It describes ways to find problems and correct their causes. It tells you how to understand the costs associated with quality and how to reduce these costs.

Quality improvement results in cost improvement. Designing and building a product right the first time always costs less. Solving problems by finding their causes and eliminating them results in measurable savings. To cash in on these savings, quality performance must be improved. This chapter describes ways to do that.

Figure 5.1 illustrates how quality cost analysis bridges the gap between the elements of a prevention-oriented quality program and the means used by company management to measure performance—the profit and loss statement. The chart shows the flow of quality cost information from the working quality assurance level to the total cost of quality level, and ultimately to the profit and loss statement. Every dollar saved because of improved quality has a direct impact on profit.

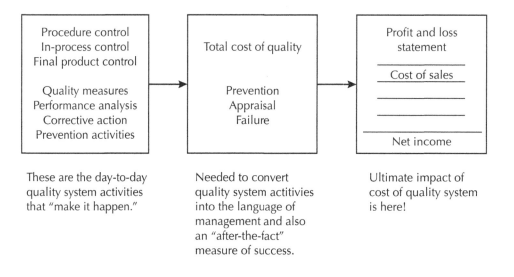

Figure 5.1 Quality cost system.

QUALITY COSTS AND THE PROFIT CENTER

Quality costs for a profit center consist of costs incurred in several activities. Figure 5.2 shows the collection of costs from all functional departments into an overall quality cost analysis for the entire profit center.

Looking at the example costs in Figure 5.2, it is obvious that quality costs are incurred by all major functions in an organization. Problem areas can exist anywhere. Careful analysis must be done to find the most costly problems and programs must be developed to attack them. Many times a strategic program is necessary. When this need exists, a strategic quality program should be developed using inputs from all functions, and it should become a part of the profit center's overall strategic program. Figure 5.3 shows the relationship between the overall strategic program and the quality program. (For the discussion on quality costs and the strategic business plan, see page 71.)

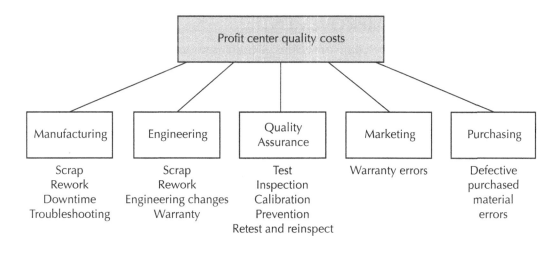

Figure 5.2   Profit center quality costs.

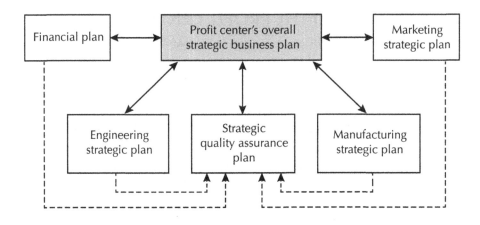

Figure 5.3   Profit center's overall strategic business plan.

PROGRAMMING IMPROVEMENT

The strategic quality plan describes a management commitment to quality and quality cost improvement. The quality cost data indicate areas that are candidates for improvement. When the highest cost areas are analyzed in greater detail, many improvement projects become apparent. For example, high warranty costs are a trigger to rank customer failure problems for detailed investigation, with the aim of identifying product design, process control, or inspection planning solutions to the highest cost problems. Regardless of what the high quality cost element may be, the mere act of identifying it should focus actions to reduce it.

Today, most management understands that there are no general solutions to quality problems (that is, to high quality cost areas). These problems are not solved by outside certifications, organizational manipulations, new management techniques, or even by quality cost analysis. The quality cost information simply identifies problem (opportunity) areas. Once the problem area is identified, the detailed nature of the problem has to be investigated and appropriate actions taken. *The entire process of quality improvement and quality cost reduction is pursued on a problem-by-problem basis.*

Because of high external failure costs, a natural temptation might be to place more emphasis on appraisal efforts, but this approach may simply convert some external failures to internal failures (such as scrap and rework) and create an increased inspection burden. For some, this can be done as a stopgap approach.

Similarly, it may be tempting to increase product engineering efforts in a generalized attempt to prevent defects, but a generalized effort may not be effective. Usually, improvements are obtained by actions in the prevention category. Effective prevention actions are those aimed at specific problems—problems that can be spotlighted by quality cost studies.

Succinctly put, the process of quality and quality cost improvement depends on understanding cause-and-effect relationships; the study of total quality costs is perhaps the most effective tool available to management to see this cause and effect.

In summary, for effective quality improvement efforts, it is necessary to:

- Recognize and organize quality-related costs to gain knowledge of magnitude, contributing elements, and trends

- Analyze quality performance, identify major problem areas, and measure product line and/or manufacturing section performance

- Implement effective corrective action and cost improvement programs

- Evaluate effect of action to assure intended results

- Program activities for maximum dollar payoff and maximum effective manpower utilization.

- Budget quality work to meet objectives

- Align activities in the prevention, appraisal, and failure cost areas to maintain the cause and effect

FINDING THE PROBLEM AREAS

When quality costs are displayed to managers who have not been exposed to the concept, the initial question is likely to be, "How much should they be?" or "How does this compare with other organizations or products?" Unfortunately, it is not practical to establish any meaningful absolute standards for such cost comparisons. A quality cost system should be tailored to a particular company's needs. This is necessary to perceive significant trends and furnish objective evidence for management decisions as to where assurance efforts should be placed for optimum return. While the search for industry guidelines or other standards of comparison is natural (in fact, benchmarking encourages this), it is quite dangerous, since it leads to quality cost emphasis of "scorecarding" rather than utilization as a management tool for improving the status quo.

The futility of establishing meaningful absolute quality cost guidelines is more apparent if you consider:

1. Inherent variations in how companies interpret and capture quality cost data

2. Critical differences in product complexity, product life cycle, process methods and stability, production volume, market characteristics, management needs and objectives, customer reactions, organizational maturity, and so on

3. The awkwardness or inappropriateness for many companies of the most prevalent form of quality cost measure (percent of net sales billed), considering the effect of time differences between time-of-sales billing and the incurrence of actual quality costs

This last factor is particularly important for periods involving an expanding or contracting product volume or mix, unstable market pricing, shifting sales / leasing revenue ratios, or changing competitive performance criteria. Accordingly, it is much more productive to abandon efforts to compare your quality cost measurements with other companies in favor of meaningful analysis of the problem areas contributing most significantly to *your* quality costs, so that suitable corrective actions can be initiated.

You would not expect your doctor to suggest a treatment plan for you based on his previous patient. Since organizations differ from each other as much as individuals do, you must have a specific approach to fit your needs.

Analysis techniques for quality costs are as varied as those used for any other quality problems in industry. They range from simple charting techniques to complicated mathematical models of the program. The most common techniques and examples of their use will be discussed here, including trend analysis and Pareto analysis by quality cost category, element, department, product, service, or other groupings.

Trend Analysis

Trend analysis is simply comparing present cost levels to past cost levels. Do collect costs for a reasonable amount of time before attempting to draw conclusions or plan action programs. The data from this minimum period should be plotted in several ways.

Costs associated with each quality cost category (prevention, appraisal, internal failure, and external failure) should be plotted periodically (for example, monthly or quarterly) as both total dollars and as a fraction of one or more measurement bases thought to be appropriate for future use as indicators of business activity. Elements contributing a high proportion of the costs within a quality cost category should be plotted and analyzed separately. Figure 5.4 contains a plot of total quality costs in a hypothetical company and plots of costs expressed as dollars per unit produced and as a percentage of sales. The graphs show that total quality costs are increasing but that total quality costs as related to units produced and sales are not changing significantly.

Figures 5.5 and 5.6 are graphs plotting quality cost categories as total dollars and as related to the same two bases. Figure 5.5 shows increases in the total dollars spent in all cost categories. Costs are stable, however, when related to the measurement bases (Figure 5.6), except for internal failure. Internal failure costs have increased slightly over the 12-month period. This indicates that further analysis of internal failure costs is needed. One useful technique for this is Pareto analysis.

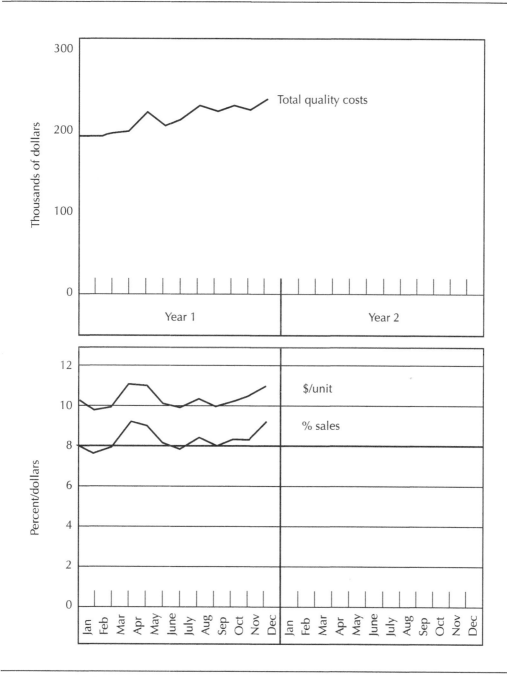

Figure 5.4   Total quality costs.

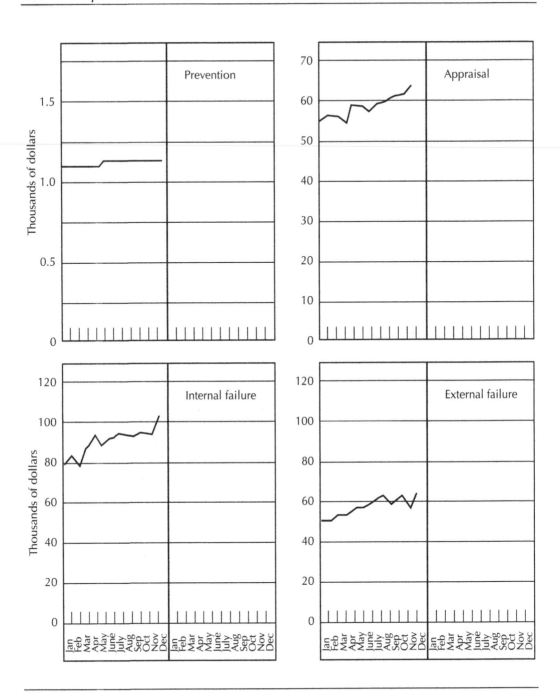

Figure 5.5 Quality costs—total dollars.

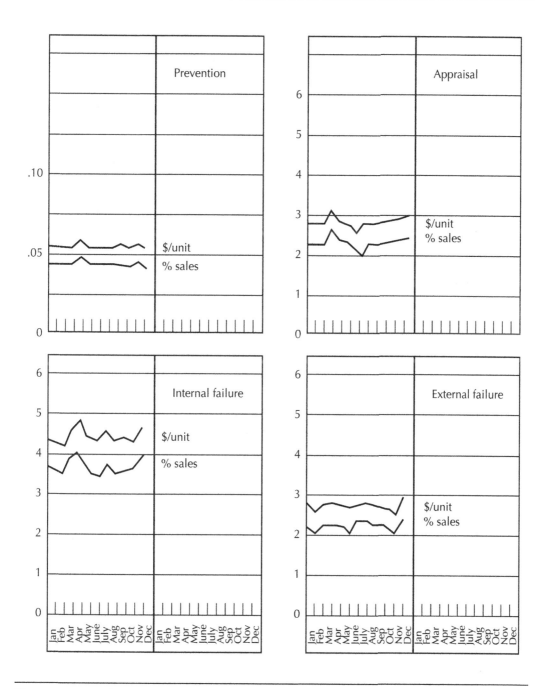

Figure 5.6   Quality costs related to bases.

Pareto Analysis

The Pareto analysis technique involves listing the factors that contribute to the problem and ranking them according to the magnitude of the contributions. In most situations, a relatively small number of causes or sources will contribute a relatively large percentage of the total costs. To produce the greatest improvement, effort should be expended on reducing costs coming from the largest contributors. In the example, the largest contributor to total costs and the one showing an increasing trend is internal failure. Figure 5.7 is a Pareto distribution showing the costs contributed by each element included in internal failure costs.

Two elements, scrap and remedial engineering, account for 69% of total internal failure costs. Pareto analysis can be used to determine where the scrap and remedial engineering costs originate. The distribution in Figure 5.8 shows that two departments in the shop account for 59% of the scrap charges. Figure 5.9 shows that 83% of the remedial engineering charges are being generated by two design engineering sections.

These distributions are typical of ones that could be found in any company. Using this sequence of techniques, high cost contributors can be identified and targeted for corrective action attention. In this example, a 10% reduction in internal failure costs by only the two highest cost contributors would mean a $75,000 cost reduction.

[$450,000 (scrap) + $300,000 (remedial engineering)] × 10% = $75,000

Objectives such as this are realistic and can be obtained if you know where to look. The Pareto analysis technique will reveal this information.

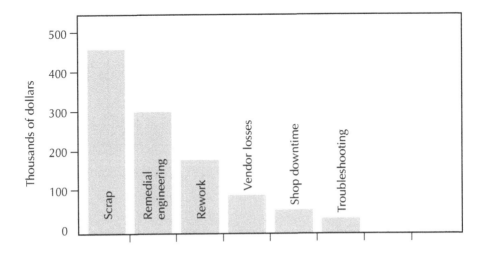

Figure 5.7   Pareto distribution of internal failure.

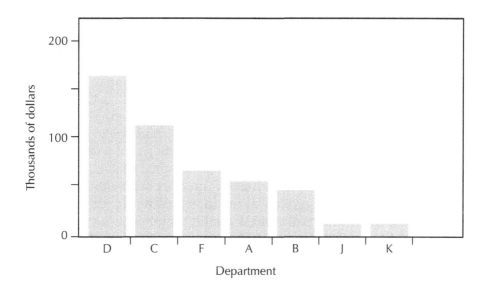

Figure 5.8   Pareto distribution of scrap.

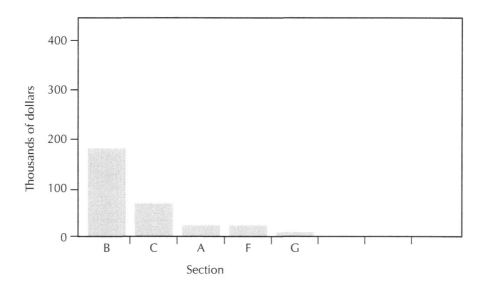

Figure 5.9   Pareto distribution of remedial engineering.

QUALITY COST ANALYSIS EXAMPLE

About the Operation

Last year, sales from the Transmotor division of PDQ Company were approximately $25 million, consisting of about 90% industrial customers and 10% government contracts. Profits after taxes were $1.2 million.

Sales increased steadily from $1.5 million in January to $2.6 million in December. This increase was due to the introduction and wide acceptance of a new product design. The new product was more reliable and cost less to produce. With a sizable amount of the new product in inventory at the start of the last year, the production rate was not increased until the second quarter.

During the year, a recently hired quality engineer started working on analysis of the quality program. He was able to improve systems and procedures, but since the middle of last year, high rejection rates on the new product (both at final assembly and on parts) forced him to spend most of his time attempting to solve some of the problems that were causing the high rejection rates.

The division's quality manager, Carl Harris, has heard about the quality costs management technique and wants to see whether it can benefit his division. Carl has attended several ASQ conferences and seminars and was able to talk with quality control managers of similar companies. It appeared to him that quality costs between 4% and 6% of net sales billed are common in companies making similar products. He is not sure, however, which cost elements are included in his competitor's quality costs. A rough calculation of his division's costs for the prior year's month of October showed:

Prevention	$ 1,000
Appraisal	100,000
Internal Failure	36,000
External Failure	27,000
Supplier Quality Cost	$164,000

Carl's first attempt at establishing a quality engineering program began over a year and a half ago with the hiring of an ASQ-certified quality engineer. Improvement of inspection methods and solutions to a few chronic quality problems have since enabled Carl to reassign several inspectors and cover the increased production load without increasing the number of inspectors in the last three-quarters of the previous year. To date, a considerable amount of 100% inspection is still being done, however, and Carl believes that more of the inspection process can be eliminated by upgrading the efficiency of the manufacturing process.

The cause of the present high rejection rate on the new product is not really known, and there is a considerable amount of finger pointing going on. Manufacturing blames a faulty design and the purchase of bad material; design engineering claims that the existing tolerances are not being met and that parts are being mishandled before they get to the assembly area. Carl decides to determine which departments are the high cost contributors by setting up a quality cost program.

Starting the Program

The first decision the quality manager must make is which unit will be covered by the study. Since there is no breakdown by profit center within the division, it is decided that the entire division will be included.

Next, the quality manager discusses the concept and proposed program with the controller and requests aid in the initial study and future reporting. The controller is skeptical of the program, but does agree to provide costs on those elements that are compiled and used for other purposes. The controller also agrees to provide personnel to aid in compiling other element costs as needed, as long as it does not interfere with their regular duties.

Now the elements to be studied must be selected. The elements shown in Figure 5.10 are selected as those most representative of the Transmotor Division operation. It is found that there are no separate accounts for some of the elements and that estimates must be made for those items. In some cases, this requires splitting amounts in a general account according to an estimated fraction of that account that is tied to the element. Some estimating can be done by counting the number of people performing such tasks as rework and sorting. Work sampling is also a valuable technique for such estimating. After determining the cost sources to use for each element, a detailed first study can be made. For the Transmotor Division, it was decided to collect data for the entire preceding year. These data are shown in Figure 5.10. The actual costs for each category are plotted in Figure 5.11.

Internal failure, appraisal, and the total costs show an upward trend, as would be expected in a period of increasing activity. Prevention costs haven't changed, but external failure costs peaked during the first half of the year and appear to be leveling off. The next step is to find appropriate measures of business activity (bases) to which to relate the data. The quality manager selected three possible bases:

- Sales base—net sales billed

- Cost base—cost of units shipped

- Labor base—factory hours

These data were collected from accounting and industrial engineering, and costs from each category were expressed as a percent of the bases chosen. Graphs of these percentages are shown as Figures 5.12, 5.13, and 5.14, respectively.

When expressed as a percent of sales, total costs, appraisal, and external failure show a downward trend while prevention and internal failure are essentially unchanged. These trends, however, are not valid, since sales data are not a good measure of the kind of activity producing the costs. Most of product billed originated from warehouse stocks for the first half of the year. Except for a December spike in quality costs as a percent of factory hours, the ratios using factory hours exhibit roughly the same trends as those using costs of units shipped (the December rise was due to a dip in factory hours because of the December holiday period). Total costs peaked about midyear and appear to be decreasing. Appraisal and external failure cost ratios display a slight downward trend. Prevention has not changed. This analysis invites attention to the increasing internal failure cost ratio. Studying this more closely, it is found that the major contributors to the increase are rework, scrap, and remedial engineering. These three elements were responsible for 91% of the internal failure costs. The largest dollar contributor is scrap, contributing 50% of the internal failure costs. Graphs of internal failure costs, as percentages of costs of units shipped, are shown in Figure 5.15.

This leads to the question, "Where are these costs being generated?" The quality manager requested a breakdown of the source of the three largest dollar contributors to the internal failure costs: scrap, rework, and remedial engineering. It was found that three sections of the shop (Winding, Feeder 1, and Feeder 5) generated 82% of the scrap during the previous year. Two sections (Winding and Assembly) contributed 73% of the rework charges, and one model (Model T) accounted for 60% of the remedial engineering. Figure 5.16 shows Pareto graphs of these cost breakdowns.

Elements	Jan	Feb	Mar	Apr	May
Prevention					
Quality planning	500	550	400	300	350
Data analysis and preventive action	500	500	600	700	650
Planning by other functions	600	400	700	750	700
Development of measurement and control equipment	0	50	0	0	0
Training	0	0	0	0	0
Quality systsem audits	0	0	0	0	0
Other prevention expenses	200	250	250	200	375
Total prevention costs	1,800	1,750	1,950	1,950	2,075
Appraisal					
Inspection & test—purchased material	5,200	5,000	5,950	4,920	5,900
Laboratory acceptance testing	925	925	925	925	925
Maint. and calibration of equipment	3,840	3,840	3,840	3,840	3,840
Depreciation of capital equipment	695	695	695	695	695
Inspection	52,300	53,250	52,275	52,325	51,250
Testing	29,120	30,950	30,050	28,245	29,350
Set-up of inspection and test	Included in "Inspection" and "Testing"				
Process and product audits	0	0	0	0	0
Checking labor	2,710	2,805	2,740	3,117	3,240
Inspection and test material	475	80	316	940	510
Outside endorsement	0	0	0	0	0
Personnel qualification	0	0	0	0	0
Review of test and inspection data	0	0	0	0	0
Field testing and inspection	0	0	0	0	0
Accumulation of cost data	0	0	0	0	0
Total appraisal costs	95,265	97,545	96,791	95,217	95,710
Internal Failure					
Scrap–division, caused	25,170	15,025	19,112	18,997	28,040
Rework–division, caused	5,200	6,150	6,210	4,925	9,010
Supplier–caused losses	1,200	1,099	1,248	1,170	1,370
Troubleshooting	2,080	1,975	2,125	2,020	2,115
Retest and reinspection	not separated from inspection costs				
Remedial engineering	4,200	4,250	7,125	8,010	7,850
Substandard product costs	0	0	0	0	0
Shop down time	Not identifiable				
Extra production operations	Not identifiable				
Total internal failure costs	37,850	28,499	35,820	35,122	48,385
External Failure					
Product warranty	19,670	22,300	22,960	24,850	22,100
Returned product cost	1,800	1,800	1,800	1,800	1,800
Field service	7,100	7,100	7,100	7,100	7,100
Total external failure costs	28,570	31,200	31,860	33,750	31,000
TOTAL QUALITY COSTS	**163,485**	**158,994**	**166,421**	**166,039**	**177,170**
MEASUREMENT BASES					
1. Net sales billed	1,525,000	1,420,500	1,872,500	1,810,200	1,798,400
2. Factory hours	82,650	83,152	82,164	81,245	82,360
3. Costs of units shipped	1,225,000	1,315,500	1,275,250	1,095,650	1,080,975

Figure 5.10 Total quality costs—Transmotor Division *(continued)*.

(continued)

June	July	Aug	Sept	Oct	Nov	Dec	Total
250	0	200	250	0	100	100	3,000
750	250	800	750	1,000	900	900	8,300
650	650	650	600	700	700	650	7,750
0	0	0	0	0	0	0	50
0	0	0	250	0	0	0	250
0	0	0	0	0	0	0	0
190	750	260	460	225	190	220	3,570
1,840	1,650	1,910	2,310	1,925	1,890	1,870	22,920
6,010	3,900	6,410	7,125	6,500	6,400	7,450	70,765
925	925	925	925	925	925	925	11,100
3,840	3,840	3,840	3,840	3,840	3,840	3,840	46,080
695	695	695	695	695	695	695	8,340
53,200	48,875	51,450	52,050	52,725	51,400	50,575	621,675
31,940	30,125	35,830	35,750	38,700	43,525	44,100	407,865
0	0	0	0	0	0	0	0
3,120	3,250	3,325	3,390	3,470	3,515	3,570	38,252
425	270	317	430	525	130	100	4,518
0	0	0	0	0	0	0	0
0	0	0	0	30	0	0	60
0	0	0	0	0	0	0	0
0	0	0	0	0	0	0	0
0	0	0	0	0	0	0	0
100,155	91,880	102,792	104,205	107,410	110,430	111,255	1,208,655
33,980	9,060	20,050	22,150	18,220	27,110	24,140	261,054
6,020	7,800	10,500	12,250	10,875	12,900	12,040	103,880
2,715	1,110	1,795	1,745	1,890	1,375	2,160	18,877
2,170	2,050	2,265	2,450	2,645	2,725	2,945	27,565
9,100	10,460	13,610	12,990	13,060	11,550	13,510	115,715
0	0	0	0	0	0	0	0
53,985	30,480	48,220	51,585	46,690	55,660	54,795	527,091
20,990	20,500	19,550	18,850	20,110	18,900	19,750	250,530
1,800	1,800	1,800	1,800	1,800	1,800	1,800	21,600
7,100	7,100	7,100	7,100	7,100	7,100	7,100	85,200
29,890	29,400	28,450	27,750	29,010	27,800	28,650	357,330
185,870	153,410	181,372	185,850	185,035	195,780	196,570	2,115,996
1,896,750	2,086,550	2,314,640	2,402,500	2,276,550	2,697,540	2,625400	24,726,530
91,200	83,750	96,750	112,750	115,750	115,700	91,250	1,118,471
1,205,620	1,125,050	1,397,450	1,334,150	1,400,500	1,602,930	1,625,625	15,683,700

Figure 5.10   Total quality costs—Transmotor Division.

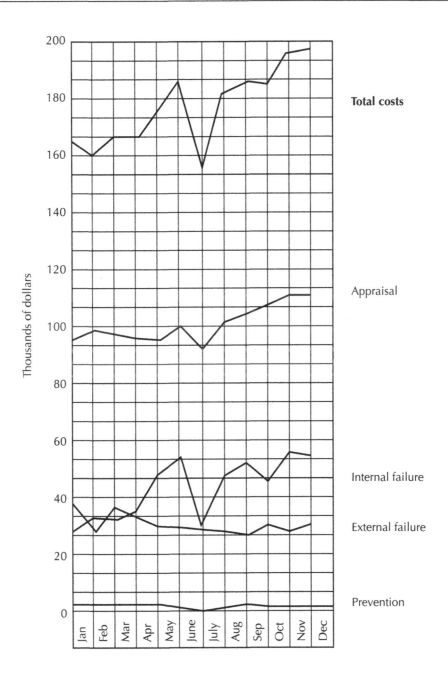

Figure 5.11   Actual quality costs.

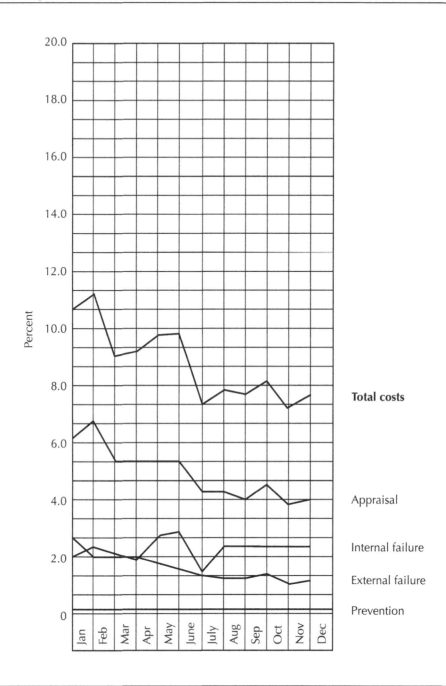

Figure 5.12 Quality costs as a percent of net sales billed.

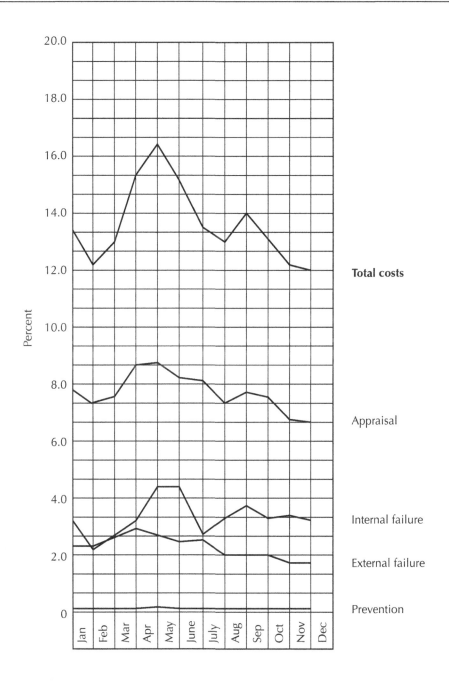

Figure 5.13   Quality costs as a percent of costs of units shipped.

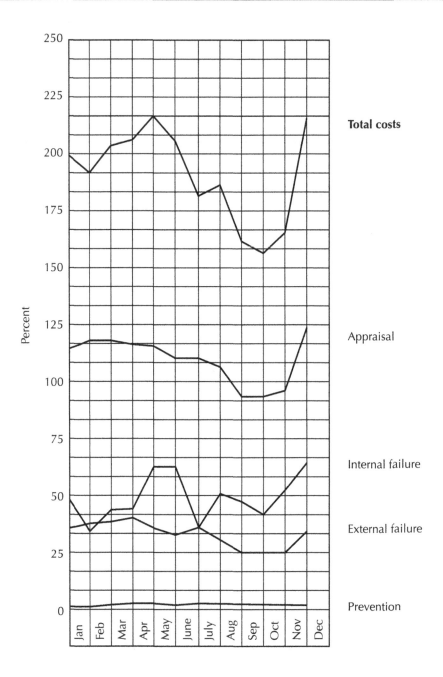

Figure 5.14 Quality costs as a percent of factory hours.

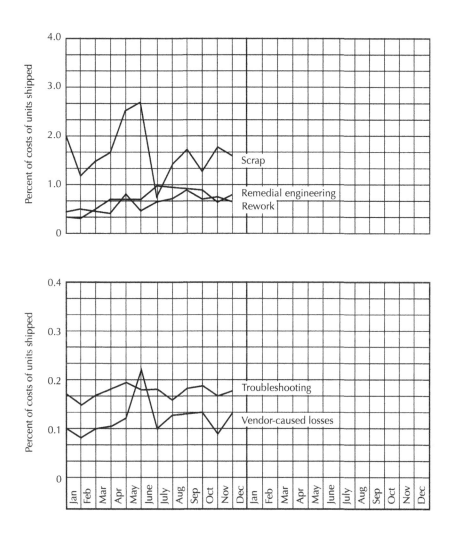

Figure 5.15   Internal failure costs.

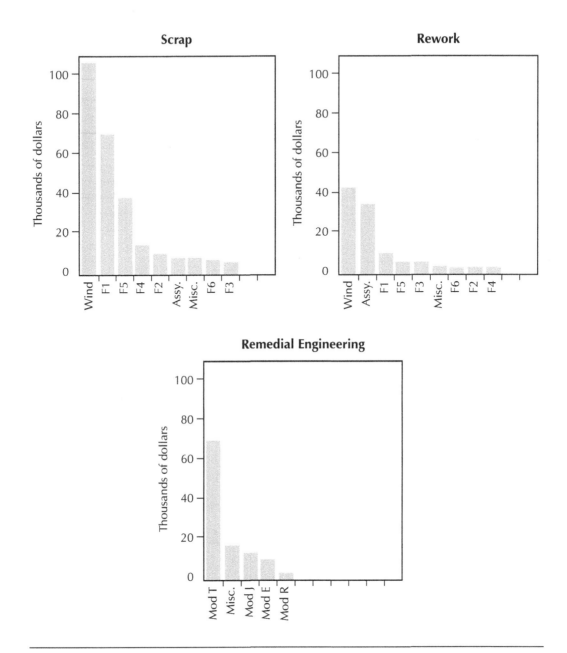

Figure 5.16   Pareto distributions of scrap, rework, and remedial engineering.

The quality manager now has enough information to begin to develop a corrective action program. To be effective, it must involve both the manufacturing manager and the engineering manager since the elements that are the largest contributors to internal failure costs are the responsibility of these functional managers. The quality manager must also examine costs that are his own responsibility—prevention and appraisal. Reductions in overall costs will require a program of cooperative effort.

A meeting is held with the responsible functional managers at which the quality manager presents the results of his study and analysis to this point. Each manager is asked for his views on the program, whether the costs for which he is responsible could be reduced, and if so, by how much. At this meeting, objectives and plans for their achievement are solicited from each responsible manager.

The initial report contains all data and graphs generated in the study, the objectives for cost reduction, and plans for reaching the objectives. Objectives developed by the management team are as follows:

1. Reduce the overall quality costs to 6.7% of net sales billed within one year

2. Reduce appraisal costs to 3.3% of net sales billed within two years, and to 3.6% within one year

3. Reduce internal failure costs to 1.8% of sales within one year

4. Maintain external failure costs at no more than 1.1%

Action programs for attainment of these objectives are as follows:

1. Hire an additional quality engineer charged with the responsibility for identification of the causes of high cost problems and coordination of corrective action.

2. Reassign the present quality engineer to the task of finding less costly ways of inspection and test and ways to eliminate 100% inspection.

3. Set up teams consisting of representatives of manufacturing, engineering, and quality in sections of the shop that have high scrap and rework costs.

4. Set up a Six Sigma task force to determine the cause of the excessive remedial engineering costs on the Model T unit. Set an objective for reduction of the costs and report progress regularly.

5. Determine the causes of the highest cost field problem. If shop-caused, assign to the shop teams for action. If caused by design or application, assign to the task force for attention. Set objectives and require reporting.

6. Issue a quality cost report each quarter showing performance against objectives and discussing major problem areas and plans for reduction of costs.

At this point we leave the Transmotor quality manager with the knowledge that he is well on his way to eliminating many of his headaches and making the quality function a profit contributor for the division.

THE TEAM APPROACH

Once a problem has been identified and reported and the involved personnel are committed to action, the job is started but far from complete. The efforts of people involved must be planned, coordinated, scheduled, implemented, and followed up. Normally, problems can be thought of as one of two types: those that one individual or department can correct with little or no outside help, and those requiring coordinated action from several activities in the organization. Examples of the first type of problem include operator-controllable defects, design errors, and inspection errors. Examples of the second type include product performance problems for which a cause is not known, defects caused by a combination of factors not under one department's control, and field failures of unknown cause.

The first type needs no elaborate system to attack and solve problems. Most can and should be resolved at the working level with the supervisor, engineer, or others. Usually, the working personnel of these departments have sufficient authority (employee empowerment) to enact corrective action, within defined limits, without specific approval.

Unfortunately, problems of the second type are normally the most costly and are not as easily solved. Causes of such problems can be numerous and unknown. Solutions may require action from several sources. The investigation of the problem and the planning of its solution must be coordinated and scheduled to assure that effective action is taken. One of the best devices for doing this is the Lean–Six Sigma or quality improvement team. Working with the data and problem analysis reports and headed by an individual who is interested in solving problems, this team develops the plan and then coordinates and schedules the investigation and action. It has been found that an interested individual with line responsibility makes the best head for such a group. Each project should be tracked. Meetings should be held regularly and minutes published. The DMAIC methodology is a good one to follow.

Case Study 1—Profit Improvement

A major electrical firm initiated a corporate program to identify, analyze, and reduce quality costs. It was called the Product Integrity Improvement (PII) program. A formal management commitment to improvement of quality and an organized approach has led to profit improvement at several divisions. This example describes the approach used and the results obtained in one location.

In most industrial environments, the greater amounts of total quality costs are found in internal and external failure costs. Therefore most organized efforts to reduce costs and improve profits are concentrated in this area. It should be stated, however, that by placing greater emphasis on the prevention activity, a significant improvement in quality costs will be realized. The PII program was intended to focus attention on all phases of quality costs and thereby improve the quality, safety, reliability, and environmental effects of products, while reducing total quality costs.

Establishing and Implementing the Division PII Program. It was decided to implement the PII program in the example division to place greater emphasis on the total quality costs. The primary events that occurred to establish and implement this program were as follows:

1. Received top management commitment, support, and involvement.

2. Organized the PII program in the division.
   a. Assigned responsibility for the PII program to a member of the division manager's immediate staff.
   b. Established a PII council to assist the PII program manager in determining the overall approach, developing division strategy, and implementing the program. The council members included the division engineering manager, manufacturing manager, controller, and quality manager.
   c. Conducted a PII seminar with headquarters quality assurance assistance to introduce the concept to responsible management personnel.

3. Identified the quality cost elements and selected account sources.

4. Collected all the quality costs for the division for the previous 12 months to establish the total quality cost baseline.

5. Analyzed the division quality cost data and identified the most significant quality cost expenditures. Analysis of the data indicated that internal failure costs were requiring a disproportionate expenditure and should receive the highest priority for action. As a result of this analysis, quality costs were found to be:

	Percent of Sales
Prevention	0.1
Appraisal	1.5
Internal Failure	2.3
External Failure	1.5
Total	5.4

Internal failure costs were analyzed to find the high cost contributors, with the following results:

Item	Approximate Percent of Total Internal Failure Cost
Cores	5
Wire	20
Coil Winding—Assembly	35
Final Assembly/Test	15
Other	25

The "Coil Winding—Assembly" area was selected since collectively it accounted for the largest portion of the total internal failure cost.

6. Determined basic problems and underlying causes of the problems and assigned responsibility for corrective action.

   a. Identified three underlying causes:
      - Operator winding errors
      - Damage to coils in handling
      - Design problems

   b. Established a quality improvement team:
      - Manufacturing manager—chairperson
      - Quality manager
      - Manufacturing engineering (equipment problems)
      - Engineering (design problems)
      - General supervisor (operator problems)

7. Established quality cost improvement objectives as an integral part of the division's profit plan.

8. Created reporting systems to provide accurate cost visibility and to measure improvement performance.

9. Met weekly to review progress, establish plans, and assign new tasks to be completed.

10. Reviewed monthly total quality costs against the objectives and initiated corrective action where needed.

11. Educated, trained, and emphasized the importance of everyone doing the job right the first time Employee involvement was most important in attempts to achieve improvement. This was accomplished in a number of ways:

    a. Established meetings with the general supervisor, quality supervisor, and section supervisors to:
       - identify key projects to be worked
       - plan programs for improvement
       - review progress

    b. Developed defect charts for each manufacturing section showing objectives and actual costs

    c. Conducted workplace meetings to establish a quality-conscious attitude

    d. Set up training programs for certain critical-skill, high-cost areas

12. Recognized individuals and/or groups that made significant contributions toward improvement.

Results obtained from this program were significant.

	Cost as a Percent of Sales		
	Previous Year Actual	Current Year Objectives	Current Year Actual
Prevention	0.1	0.1	0.1
Appraisal	1.5	1.3	1.2
Internal failure	2.3	2.0	2.1
External failure	1.5	1.1	1.2
Total	5.4	4.5	4.6

Summary. The success of a PII program depends upon a number of factors:

- Top management involvement and support
- Visible total quality cost data
- The setting of division objectives for improvement and monthly reporting of performance against objectives
- Organization for improvement
- The establishment of a quality improvement team
- Employee involvement and recognition

The benefits to be gained from a properly implemented PII program include:

- Reduced total quality costs with a corresponding increase in profits
- Improved product performance, product integrity, and adherence to schedule
- Increased customer acceptance of products and services
- Increased repeat sales and new sales from improved product reputation

Case Study 2—Failure Cost Improvement

A major connector manufacturer elected to enter the connector market with a new connector design to Department of Defense (DoD) requirements. The following discussion illustrates how in four years the product assembly failure cost was reduced form $180,000 per year to $20,000 per year.

History. During the program's early phases, typical start-up problems associated with new manufacturing techniques, planning, and training occurred. These items were resolved one by one until assembly failure costs decreased to approximately $180,000, an amount that is still considered above normal for a new connector program.

Three years later, a failure costs plateau of $150,000 per year had been reached, a figure that still was comparatively high. It was not known that a considerable portion of failure dollars originated in the assembly departments. Using the financial data available, failure costs by specific cost center in the assembly departments were identified. (Each cost center is responsible for the assembly of a specific connector type.)

It was observed that two specific cost centers contributed to more than 75% of the assembly departments' total failure costs through that period. One major cost center was where bonded assemblies for other connectors are manufactured. This area was also the target for major cost improvements.

Using the first half of the year as a base and holding sales constant through the second half of the year, it became apparent that another large dollar failure cost year would result in the connector area (Table 5.1). It was necessary to attack the problem immediately.

Approach. A review of the prior six months' failure history was initiated. All discrepancy reports were evaluated, summarized, and categorized, and high scrap and rework cost areas were found (Figure 5.17).

It was apparent from this summary that nearly 85% of all rejections occurred as the result of parts contaminated by improperly applied or excessively applied adhesives. Because of the amount of labor needed to remove the adhesives, on average 80 connectors per month were scrapped. This alone amounted to almost $20,000 per year.

Table 5.1 Failure costs by cost center.

	CC:2441 (Bonding) ($ 000)	CC:2450 (Connector Assembly) ($ 000)
First half year 1	57.6	67.0
Second half year 1	17.7	34.0
Total year 1	75.3	101.0
Total year 2	41.2	22.0
Net savings	**34.1**	**79.0**

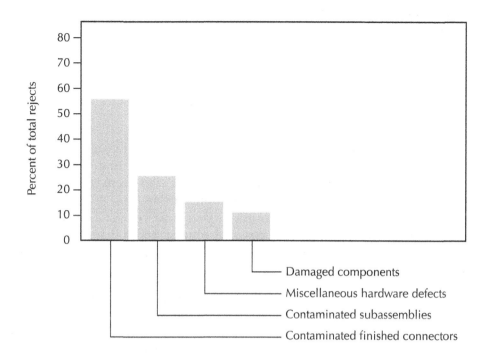

Figure 5.17   Rejection causes.

Cause. Based on the data, these causes were identified:

1. Methods employed for the application of adhesives for this new connector series were outdated.

2. Operators required additional training in the application of adhesives.

3. Operators and inspectors did not understand the complete workmanship standards developed for this program. As a result, the operators were performing unnecessary rework.

As a result of these causes, some of the operators were causing a larger percentage of rework and scrap than others.

Corrective Measures. Once the causes were identified, a corrective action team was formed to include a quality engineer, an industrial engineer, and the production supervisor. The production supervisor was appointed to head the team. They accomplished a number of important changes:

1. They reviewed manufacturing instructions, revised methods, obtained new tools, and revised workmanship standards.

2. They introduced a new method for the application of adhesives by means of a silk screen technique.

3. They retrained or replaced the operators causing the most rework and scrap.

4. They retrained inspectors and operators in the requirements of the modified workmanship standards.

Costs for these changes were approximately $4,000 in tooling and $3,000 in labor.

Results. Table 5.1 compares the results of the first half of year 1 to the second half of year 1. Failure costs in this area decreased dramatically. Note that failure dollars in the bonded assembly cost center also decreased as a result of application of techniques learned in the connector area.

Table 5.1 also compares the results of year 1 to year 2. The results have yielded a net savings in failure costs of almost $80,000 for year 2 in the connector area despite increased sales volume. There was also a $34,000 savings in the bonding area.

Summary. By using the tools available, the team was able to identify a problem, determine its cause, and initiate corrective action to prevent recurrence. This resulted in a net savings equivalent to a sales increase of over $350,000 on these products. This was accomplished by recognizing that small pieces of a larger problem can more easily be digested and resolved one at a time.

TEAM-BASED PROBLEM SOLVING

Quality costs techniques are especially useful for quality improvement teams, enabling them to quantify the financial impact of their projects for themselves and for management. The following example integrates quality costs with team problem solving and, although taken from a service organization, works equally well for manufacturing organizations.

Step 1. Form or Select Cross-Functional Teams

The best way to obtain management support is to show how team-based quality cost techniques can improve the organization's "bottom line." By focusing on key business processes such as order administration, new product development, sales, service, or manufacturing, the team can use quality cost measurements to show an "as is" versus a "could be" performance baseline.

Let's use customer complaints as an example of a problem to be solved and form a team to address this issue. A cross-functional team for this problem might include team members from sales (the team leader), customer service, manufacturing, engineering, and quality.

Step 2. Initiate Problem Solving

To be successful with team-based quality cost techniques, team members must understand basic problem solving techniques. This includes how to write problem statements, develop cause-and-effect diagrams (also known as Ishikawa and "fishbone" diagrams), and brainstorm for potential root causes of problems.

Typically the quality professional is the key person who will plan for and propose that team-based quality cost techniques be undertaken. Usually the quality professional is already familiar with the concept of quality costs and problem solving. If needed, training should be obtained for the quality costs project leader and/or implementation team on the principles of quality costs. A quality costs refresher course can be most helpful to open the thought process and generate new ideas.

In this example, the team decided to look at the types of customer complaints and how often they occurred. This information can usually be obtained from customer service or quality departments, which are likely tracking complaints by type. In our example, the team decides to look at a specific customer complaint—"no power-up"—based on the fact that it occurred frequently and directly impacted the external customer.

The team's brainstorming created the cause-and-effect diagram illustrated in Figure 5.18.

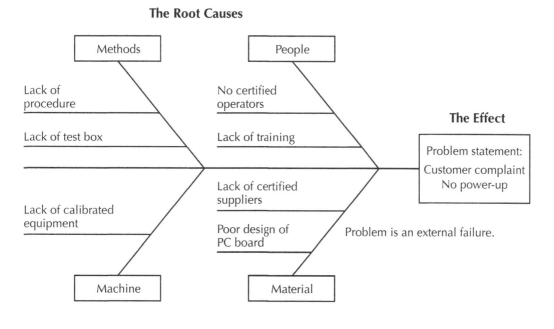

Figure 5.18   Cause-and-effect diagram.

Step 3. Calculate the Failure Cost of One Occurrence

Once cause-and-effect diagram(s) have been developed and brainstorming for root cause has taken place, it's time to calculate the cost of one occurrence for the problem selected. A cost of quality worksheet can be created like the one shown in Table 5.2.

When creating a cost of quality worksheet, simple is best. Initially, include only the basic tasks that must be performed to find and fix the problem. Be sure to list times in the "Average Hours per Task" column in decimal hours. Task time can be obtained by using industrial engineering estimates or by simply asking the people involved in the corrective action process. Remember these are averages; they need not be exact measurements. Quality cost reporting should be used for management reporting, not for detailed financial reporting; hence, solid estimates are acceptable.

The "Hourly Rate" column is the average "loaded" hourly rate, including benefits, for the department performing the task. This rate can be obtained from the finance department. If such information is not available, simply determine the average hourly rate by dividing the total wages charged to the department by the number of employees in the department. For example, if

Table 5.2   Cost of quality worksheet.

Tasks	Average Hours per Task	Hourly Rate	Cost of Element	Material Costs	External Failure ($)	Internal Failure ($)	Total Failure Cost
1. Customer Service answers phone and records information	0.10	$35.00	$3.50	N/A	$3.50	N/A	$3.50
2. Forwards info to Quality Assurance	0.10	$35.00	$3.50	N/A	$3.50	N/A	$3.50
3. Q/A investigates the problem	1.50	$50.00	$75.00	N/A	$75.00	N/A	$75.00
a. Q/A performs destructive test on another stock part	0.50	$50.00	$25.00	N/A	$25.00	N/A	$25.00
b. Cost of part	N/A	N/A	N/A	$43.63	$43.63	N/A	$43.63
4. Fix process in manufacturing	2.25	$50.00	$112.50	N/A	$112.50	N/A	$112.50
5. Contact customer with fix and new part	0.75	$50.00	$37.50	N/A $43.63	$37.50 $43.63	N/A N/A	$37.50 $43.63
Total							$344.26

six people work in the customer service department and the weekly payroll is $8,350, the average hourly rate is $8,350 divided by 40 hours/week, equaling $208.75/hour. Divided by six people, this equals $34.80/hour per person. In the example, the average hourly rate of $35/hour is used for the customer service department. If more than one person is involved in the process, multiply the number of employees by the figure in the "Cost of Element" column. A similar approach is taken for other departments involved in the process.

The "Cost of Element" column contains the result of the average hours per task multiplied by the hourly rate. The "Material Costs" column contains those expenses that are true out-of-pocket costs such as inventory items, part costs, unplanned travel expenses, or other real "receipted" expenses.

When deciding whether the cost of the problem is an external or internal failure, simply note where the defect is found. All external failures are found by the customer and all cost calculations remain in the "External Failure" column. The cost is either all external or all internal failure, not a mixture of the two. The costs are then added horizontally across the worksheet and totaled in the "Total Failure Cost" column. The total cost of one occurrence in this example is $344.26, which is obtained by summing the final column.

It is helpful to code the problem. In this example, "EF-NP" is used and recorded in the upper right corner of the worksheet to abbreviate the problem description of "Customer Complaint—No Power-Up—External Failure." Such coding is useful when an application is used for trend analysis.

Step 4. Calculate the Total Failure Cost for a Given Period

Now that the cost of one occurrence for the problem has been calculated, it's necessary to determine the actual frequency of occurrence. This information can usually be obtained from quality problem or defect reports such as customer service call-in logs and inspection sheets or from audit reports.

In this example, if we had 48 occurrences in one year, the total external failure cost for "Customer Complaints—No Power-Up" would be $16,524.48 annually ($344.26 multiplied by 48 occurrences). A problem that appeared insignificant or tolerable now merits attention using quality cost failure dollars.

Step. 5 Rank Problems by Failure Dollars using Pareto Analysis

You can now repeat the costing process for several other problems or defect types. Both the number of occurrences and the cost of quality for both internal and external failures can be viewed. The approach becomes easier as it is repeated.

In the example, the failure cost Pareto analysis worksheet, ranked by annual failure costs, would look like Table 5.3.

Table 5.3   Pareto analysis of failure costs.

Problem Description	Failure Type	Annual Failure $	No. of Annual Occurrences
No power-up	EF	$16,524.48	48
Computer downtime	IF	$11,838.11	20
Order shipped late	EF	$9,333.58	36
Paperwork incomplete	IF	$6,423.15	121

EF = External Failure   IF = Internal Failure

Notice that the most frequently occurring problem or defect does not always have the highest failure cost. Taking corrective action on the "No Power-Up" problem selected by the team will give the most return. Quality cost analysis helps prioritize problem solving activities. Of course, considerations such as customer criticality, complexity, and ease and timeliness of solution also come into play. But before investing much time or money in solutions, it is important to have quality cost data showing significant financial impact.

Step 6. Look at the Cause-and-Effect Diagram and Propose a Prevention Plan

It's now time to propose a plan for the application of prevention resources to eliminate the problem's root causes. A cause-and-effect diagram similar to the one illustrated in Figure 5.18 will be useful.

Using our "Customer Complaints—No Power-Up" example, which had an external failure cost of $16,524.48 annually, and the associated cause-and-effect diagram (Figure 5.18), it's possible to calculate the proposed prevention costs as illustrated in Table 5.4.

Table 5.4 Proposed prevention plan and costs.

Root Cause Description	Proposed Tasks to Eliminate	Hours Needed	$ Rate	Total $
Lack of procedure	Write procedure	3.0	$ 50/hr	$150
No certified operators and lack of training	Train and certify operators	40.0	$ 35/hr	$1,400
Lack of calibrated equipment	Calibrate equipment	2.0	$35/hr	$ 70
Lack of a test box	Make a test box	4.4	$50/hr	$220
Lack of certified suppliers	Find ISO-registered supplier	2.0	$35/hr	$ 70
Poor design of PC Board	None	N/A	N/A	N/A
Total prevention investment required				**$1,910**

Step 7. Set Team Goal for Reducing Frequency of Occurrence

The next step is for the problem solving team to estimate the level of occurrence reduction they believe is possible, if the proposed prevention resources were made available. Depending on the complexity of the problem and the associated cause-and-effect relationship, some teams may commit to a 100% reduction (goal of zero defects), while others may commit to something less. Be careful not to over-commit. Should something outside the control of the team occur, an aggressive goal can be discouraging to the team and commitment can diminish.

In the example, the team selected a 50% reduction goal for the problem of "No Power-Up," hoping to reduce the number of occurrences from 48 to 24 per year and eliminating an annual external failure cost of $16,524.48.

Step 8. Calculate the Return on Investment (ROI) and Payback Period

Once the reduction goal is set and the prevention plan developed, you can calculate the return on investment (benefit/cost) and payback period (the time it takes to break even on the investment spent on prevention). This is done for each problem selected and can be calculated using a worksheet like the one shown in Figure 5.19.

The example shows the external failure cost of 48 occurrences for the problem of "No Power–Up," which totals $16,524.48 annually. An additional $500 was added for unplanned premium freight charges (obtained from the finance department), resulting in a total external failure cost of $17,024.48. Recall that the team assigned to this problem committed to reducing the number of occurrences to 24, a 50% reduction, or $8,512.24. This is shown in the figure as the annual achievable failure reduction.

Customer complaint—no power-up

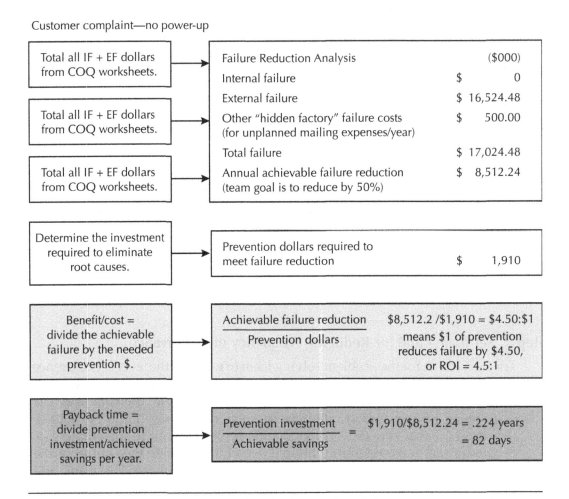

Figure 5.19   Return on investment and payback period worksheet.

Recall from the prevention plan above that the prevention dollars proposed is $1910. The benefit/cost ratio is then calculated by dividing achievable failure reduction dollars by prevention dollars ($8,512.24/$1910), a ratio of 4.5:1. This means a return on investment of $4.50 for every dollar invested. When compared to other problems, or perhaps even those assigned to other teams, this problem could be selected as one worth pursuing.

The payback period is calculated simply by taking the inverse of the benefit/cost ratio. In the example, $1910/$8,512.24 equals a payback period of 0.224 years or 82 days. This means that the prevention investment of $1950 will pay for itself in less than three months. Again, comparing this calculation to other problems could prove it a worthwhile pursuit.

Both the return on investment and the payback period calculations can be used to select the problem with the highest return and shortest payback period, helping teams show management the results of effective problem solving.

Step 9. Make Presentation to Management

Using the return on investment and payback period worksheet (Figure 5.19), the team can now make a presentation to management requesting that the prevention funds be authorized. This format is particularly useful when other teams are seeking the same prevention funds. Prevention funds are limited and usually the funding of all improvement projects at the same time is not feasible. By using this worksheet, management can evaluate and select problems to pursue based on which have the highest return on investment with the shortest payback period. It may even be possible to add to the prevention funds if the payback is short enough.

Step 10. Track Progress and Repeat Process on Another Problem

As with any quality improvement project, progress must be measured and tracked. The technique presented here offers a simple approach: counting the number of occurrences. When occurrences decrease, the cost of quality will also show a decrease. Numbers can easily be summarized by week, by month, or by other selected reporting periods. After the plan has been implemented and progress has been made, the team can repeat this quality cost problem solving process to make further improvements in the company.

Implementation Guidelines

Four guidelines should be considered when implementing team-based cost of quality problem solving techniques:

1. The team-based quality cost problem solving technique is centered on the identification of a problem and tasks that result each time a problem occurs. These tasks are then assessed under the traditional quality cost definitions of external and internal failure. The total cost of the problem on a per occurrence basis results.

2. Team-based quality cost problem solving techniques should be used with existing or planned teams. Don't "reinvent the wheel" or call this a "new and improved quality program." Make quality costs part of the team's weekly or monthly reporting process.

3. Finance should review and approve calculation worksheets and any assumptions. Don't create a new accounting system. Team-based quality cost problem solving techniques are not intended to modify or replace the existing accounting system. Its calculations are estimates, but determined with logic and rationale. Existing "appraisal" systems can be used to capture the frequency of occurrence and are likely to be readily available.

4. Provide training. Some users experience difficulty with team-based problem solving when first introduced to the technique.

Conclusion

The methodology presented here is a roadmap showing how quality costs can be calculated by problem solving teams. It provides a focus to process improvement teams, managers, and others who are involved in quality improvement.

WORKING WITH SUPPLIERS TO REDUCE SUPPLIER QUALITY COSTS

There are always suppliers that stand out by creating difficulties. Some companies debit suppliers for the scrap and rework occurring in the buyer's plant in order to place responsibility for failure where it hurts most—in the pocketbook. In the long run, however, this may be counterproductive because some suppliers will ask for a price increase (or allow a price increase to creep in) to cover this situation. Another method often used by the buyer is to reduce the amount of business given to the offending supplier, rewarding better suppliers with a greater "share of the pie."

A more positive approach is to use supplier quality costs to identify needed supplier quality improvements. This approach can help strengthen team work and trust between supplier and buyer. Better information exchange will help both firms reduce costs. The buying company can then initiate projects jointly with suppliers to resolve the problems that are the source of high quality costs.

Perhaps the problems can be solved through buying company actions. Maybe the specifications are incorrect, or the seller really doesn't know the application of this component in the total product. Ensuring correct specifications helps to assure the procurement of good parts and also helps to assure that good parts are not wrongly rejected.

In other cases, it may be that the seller's manufacturing process needs upgrading through better tooling. Through joint projects using supplier quality costs as facts, these problems can be solved, resulting in better products and lower costs to both parties.

As was discussed in Chapter 4, a company should consider quality costs in its supplier relationships. This will allow the buying company to determine the costs and suppliers on which to focus attention. The buying company can suggest to these suppliers that they adopt a quality cost program, if appropriate, or perform special quality studies to obtain improvements in product quality. However, care must be used. Small companies may not be able to support this effort and there may be special circumstances at play in other companies that would prohibit a successful application. Supplier quality costs can also be used by the buying company as a basis for starting joint quality improvement projects with its suppliers.

Most important of all is that any quality costs program is incomplete without an effective corrective action program. The mere act of collecting quality costs will do nothing for your company but add costs. Only through pinpointing and permanently solving problems can a company progress in improving quality and productivity while reducing costs.

GAINING JUSTIFICATION FROM CUSTOMER SATISFACTION[1]

Quality cost techniques can be supplemented to justify changes for improving customer satisfaction. The monetary gain a company receives by having satisfied customers can be quantified. A satisfied customer is more willing to repurchase from a company. The payoff is a gain in repeat sales and an accompanying increase in cash flow at some time in the future.

Background

In order to have an effective continuous improvement effort, a company must have certain values and beliefs, including:

1. A focus on buyers and their needs

2. A recognition that quality is determined by the buyer

3. An awareness that problem prevention is of primary importance

In a continuous improvement environment, quality cost techniques must focus on the buyer. The approach described here supports continuous improvement efforts. It recognizes that buyer perceptions form the benchmark of quality. It also provides justification for changes that can prevent problems that affect the buyer.

Buyer Satisfaction

Like beauty, quality is in the eye of the beholder. In this case, the beholder is the buyer. This perception of a buyer is of great importance to a company. A satisfied customer will have a greater willingness to repurchase from a company in the future. This relationship is shown in Figure 5.20.

Figure 5.20   Repurchase intentions based on perception of quality.

Source: aBased on data from marketing study (J.M. Juran and F.M. Gryna. *Quality Planning and Analysis*, 3rd ed., New York: McGraw-Hill, Inc. 1993, page 87).

Payoff

The potential monetary gain, or payoff, a company experiences because it has satisfied customers is often quite large. A satisfied customer has a much greater willingness to repurchase. Because this payoff may be sometime in the future and not immediate, the company must have a long-range outlook.

In contrast, the penalties for buyer dissatisfaction are severe. An unhappy buyer could tell as many as 35 people about the problem and this secondary effect may have a severe impact on future sales.

Gain in contribution margin is the payoff a company experiences by improving customer satisfaction. Gain in contribution margin is defined as cash flow from the incremental gain in revenue minus incremental increase in cost due to additional repeat sales from more satisfied customers.

The following steps are suggested to calculate the gain in contribution margin resulting from a projected increase in buyer satisfaction:

1. *Find the relationship between buyers' perception of quality and repurchase intentions.* This requires a marketing study involving the current buyer base. The buyers chosen for the survey should be those likely to repurchase soon. Ask buyers to rate how they feel about the quality of the product and then ask whether they are willing to repurchase a similar product. Figure 5.21 shows the results of such a study.

2. *Determine when repurchases are likely to be made.* For most companies, repurchases are made near the end of the life cycle of the product. This is usually well beyond the warranty period. For some companies, sales records may contain this information. For others, a marketing study of the current customer base may be required. Ask buyers when they expect to repurchase a similar product. Figure 5.21 is a profile of buyers' repurchase intentions. All buyers initially purchased the product at time "0." Note that each company and each product within a company may have a different profile.

3. *Assess the current perception of buyers regarding the quality of the product.* This also requires a marketing study of the customer base. To reduce the effort, the marketing studies suggested in these three steps may be combined into one survey. For this step, ask buyers to rate how they feel about the product. Figure 5.22 illustrates the results of such a study. Note that only 30% of customers rated the product good or better. Many would feel that this leaves room for significant improvement in customer satisfaction.

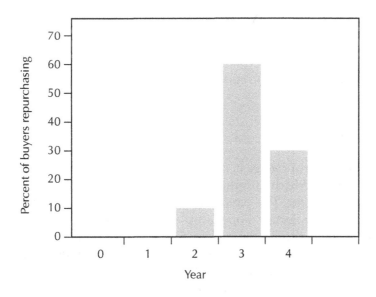

Figure 5.21   Profile of when buyers in year 0 will repurchase.

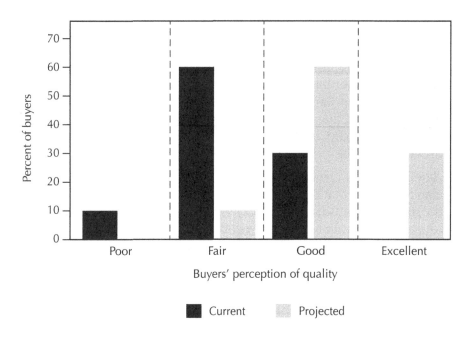

Figure 5.22   Buyers' current perceptions of quality and projected perceptions after proposed increase in customer satisfaction.

4. *Project the desired change in customer perceptions of quality before making improvements.* Much judgment is required as to what level of satisfaction should be sought. The payoff for a company is contingent on the size of the increase projected. For example, a larger increase will result in more monetary gain from repeat sales. On the other hand, a larger increase will be more challenging to obtain. Aiding in this judgment is knowledge of the current level of customer satisfaction (as found in Step 3). Comparing customer satisfaction with owners of competitive products may also be useful and a marketing study is necessary. Figure 5.22 also contains the projected perceptions of quality after a proposed increase in customer satisfaction. Note that customer perceptions are projected to be one notch up after improvements are made.

Table 5.5   Buyer's adjusted willingness to repurchase with current levels of customer satisfaction.

Buyers' Perception	% Willing to Repurchase	% of Buyers	Adjusted % Willing to Repurchase
Poor	0	10	0
Fair	18	60	10.8
Good	62	30	18.6
Excellent	92	0	0
Composite % Willing to Repurchase		100	29.4

5. *Calculate the percentage of buyers willing to repurchase under current levels of customer satisfaction.* The calculation of current levels of customer satisfaction, in terms of "composite % willing to repurchase," is shown in Table 5.5. Sources of data in this table are:

Column	Label	Source of Data
1	Buyers' Perception	Figure 5.20
2	% Willing to Repurchase	Figure 5.20
3	% of Buyers	Figure 5.22

The product of columns 2 and 3 is entered in the fourth column ("Adjusted % willing to repurchase") after converting from necessary percentages to decimals. The total of the entries in the fourth column comprises the "Composite % willing to repurchase."

This measure of the current level of customer satisfaction is a weighted average of the data for the various perceptions. Table 5.5 shows that only 29.4% of buyers are currently willing to repurchase.

6. *Calculate the percent of buyers willing to repurchase under the projected levels of customer satisfaction.* A similar calculation can be made for the projected levels of customer satisfaction (Table 5.6). The sources of data and the calculations are identical to that described in Step 5. The measure of the projected level of customer satisfaction ("Composite % willing to repurchase") shows that 66.6% are now likely to repurchase.

7. *Calculate the gain in percent of buyers willing to repurchase if projected levels of customer satisfaction are obtained.* The gain in buyers willing to repurchase is 37.2%, the difference between "Composite % willing to repurchase" found in Step 6 (66.6%) and that found in Step 5 (29.4 %). In other words, repeat sales from the projected increase in buyer satisfaction more than doubled.

8. *Calculate the gain in contribution margin for each year repurchases are made if projected levels of customer satisfaction are obtained.* Table 5.7 illustrates the calculation made for the gain in contribution margin if projected levels of customer satisfaction are obtained.

Table 5.6   Buyers' willing to repurchase with proposed improvement in customer satisfaction.

Buyers' Perception	% Willing to Repurchase	% of Buyers	Adjusted % Willing to Repurchase
Poor	0	0	0
Fair	18	10	1.8
Good	62	60	37.2
Excellent	92	30	27.6
Composite % Willing to Repurchase		100	66.6

Table 5.7   Calculated gain in contribution margin due to gain in repeat sales through proposed improvement in customer satisfaction.

Year	% Buyers Repurchasing	Gain in % Willing to Repurchase	Volume Bought Year 0	Contr. Margin $/Unit	Gain Total Contr. Margin
0	0				
1	0				
2	10	37.2	200,000	4.75	35,340
3	60	37.2	200,000	4.75	212,040
4	30	37.2	200,000	4.75	106,020

The sources of data for the columns in this table are:

Column	Label	Source of Data
1	Year	Figure 5.19
2	% of Buyers	Figure 5.20
3	Gain in % Willing to Repurchase	Step 7
4	Volume Bought Year 0	Sales Records
5	Contr. Margin $/Unit	Cost Accounting

The product of columns 2 through 5 for each row is entered in column 6 ("Gain total contr. margin"). Note that this calculation requires converting percentages to decimals. The payoff for the company or gain in total contribution margin is shown for years 2 through 4. This is when buyers will make repurchases. However, investment resulting in better buyer satisfaction would mostly be made in year 0—the year the product is built and sold. For this example, the payoff in repeat sales and added cash flow will be realized from two to four years after the product is built and sold. This requires a long-range outlook on justification of investments for improved customer satisfaction.

9. *Find the present worth in year 0 of gain in contribution margin for future years.* Investments to improve customer satisfaction must be made mostly in year 0 of the product life prior to shipping. Therefore the present worth in year 0 of the benefits listed in Table 5.7 for years 2 through 4 must be calculated. This will allow an "apples to apples" comparison of the benefits to the cost of making the necessary changes required in year 0. Figure 5.23 shows this relationship. Engineering economic principles (Newnan 1991) can be used to make this calculation. For the example, assuming a 10% compound interest factor, the calculation is:

Present Worth = Sum (Future Amount x Compound Amount Factor)

(Year 2)	=	$35,340	×	.8264	=	$29,205
(Year 3)	=	$212,040	×	.7513	=	$159,306
(Year 4)	=	$106,020	×	.6830	=	$72,412
(Year 0)	=					$260,923

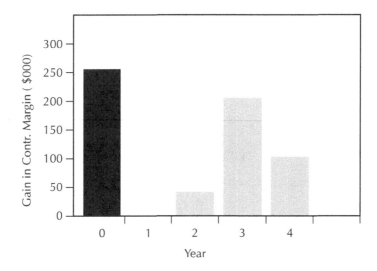

Figure 5.23 Present worth in year 0 of gain in contribution margin through increased repeat sales in years 2–4. Additional repeat sales projected by proposed increase in customer satisfaction. A compound interest factor of 10% was assumed.

Source: Newnan, Donald G. 1991. *Engineering Economic Analysis,* 4th ed., San Jose: Engineering Press, Inc.

Justification

More than $260,000 has been identified by the new approach for justification of changes leading to improvement of customer satisfaction. This is in addition to funds that may be identified by traditional quality cost techniques.

Traditional quality cost techniques may identify other funds supporting changes leading to improved customer satisfaction through reductions in several areas:

- *Warranty claims.* The total cost of claims paid to the buyer or user, after acceptance, to cover expenses including repair costs such as removing defective hardware from a system or cleaning costs due to a food or chemical service accident. Where a price reduction is negotiated in lieu of warranty, the value of the reduction should be counted.

- *Liability costs.* Company-paid costs due to liability claims including the cost of product or service liability insurance.

- *Penalties.* The cost of any penalties incurred because of less than full product or service performance (as required by contracts with buyers or by government rules and regulations).

- *Buyer/user goodwill.* Costs incurred, over and above normal selling costs, to buyers or users who are not completely satisfied with the quality of delivered product or service.

Investment

Long ago the definitions of quality costs were adapted for work beyond manufacturing. The definitions of cost correspond to activities in the quality system for producing a product or service. This starts in marketing and extends through the other functions relating to product development and production. In view of this, quality cost definitions are used to show where possible investments can be made to upgrade customer satisfaction.

About 80% of the perception of buyer satisfaction depends upon whether a product meets the true needs of the buyer. The funds identified could justify important improvements in assessing buyer needs and then validating that these needs are met. Improvements may be in the following quality activities:

- *Marketing/buyer/user.* Costs incurred in the accumulation and continued evaluation of buyer and user quality needs and perceptions (including feedback on reliability and performance) affecting their satisfaction with the company's product or service. This includes:
  - Marketing research
  - Buyer/user perception surveys/clinics
  - Contract/document review
- *Product/service design development.* Costs incurred to translate buyer and user needs into reliable quality standards and requirements and manage the quality of new product or service developments prior to the release of authorized documentation for initial production. This includes:
  - Design quality progress reviews
  - Design support activities
  - Product design–qualification test
  - Service Design–qualification field trials
- *Special product evaluations.* Includes life testing and environmental and reliability tests performed on production units.

The remaining 20% of the perception of buyer satisfaction is influenced by how a company handles complaints and solves problems. The funds identified could also justify desirable changes for these activities. This may include:

- *Evaluation of field stock and spare parts.* Includes cost of evaluation testing or inspection of field stock resulting from engineering changes, storage time (excessive shelf life), or other suspected problems.
- *Complaint investigations/buyer or user service.* The total cost of investigating, resolving, and responding to individual buyer or user complaints or inquiries, including necessary field service.
- *Retrofit costs.* Costs to modify or update products or field service facilities to a new design change level, based on major redesign due to design deficiencies.

Although not a quality cost, improvement of customer satisfaction may also require an investment in upgrading the product or processes involved in making the product.

Conclusions

Looking at how customer satisfaction links to quality cost measurement, we can conclude:

1. Quantifying the monetary gain to a company that satisfies customers provides significant justification for making improvements affecting customer satisfaction.

2. Companies using this approach must have a long range outlook. The monetary gain occurs in the future in the form of repurchases.

3. Future monetary gain must be equated to the present to match when investments for improvements will be made. This can be done using engineering economics principles. By doing this, an "apples to apples" comparison can be made between investment costs and expected benefits or monetary gain.

4. The suggested approach expands costing techniques by providing an analysis that is customer focused. This type of analysis is more in tune with continuous improvement, Lean, and Six Sigma approaches being used.

End Note

1. Material for this section was extracted from "Driving Buyer Satisfaction by Quality Cost" by William O. Winchell, published in the *Transactions of the 50th ASQC Annual Quality Congress,* ASQ Milwaukee, 1996.

Chapter 6

Service and Software Case Studies

Although most examples and case studies provided throughout this text apply equally well to both manufacturing and service industry organizations, they were obtained primarily from manufacturing concerns. To even the score for our service and software readers, case studies obtained from actual service and software development operations have been included in this chapter.

BANKING

Eleven business units of Banc One Corporation participated in a study of quality costs, customer satisfaction, and quality deficiencies/defects. The relationship between these three measurable components of quality was explored. Correlation analysis was performed using these three metrics. Interesting relationships emerged that can help predict what you will find and improve in an organization if each one of the metrics is measured over time.

Attacking high cost of quality opportunities reduces cost, defects, and errors and significantly increases customer satisfaction—and delight. A cost of quality analysis helps prioritize the opportunities for improvement. This prioritization process assures the selection of those opportunities that will have the biggest impact on the bottom line. The quality improvement team processes used to attack cost of quality opportunities will be discussed (see Figure 6.1). Banc One uses this process on an ongoing basis to allocate resources and to motivate or assign quality improvement teams to improve opportunities. In recent years, they have enhanced net income by $20 million annually through the application of these processes.

Introduction

Within the service industry, as within manufacturing concerns, there are costs associated with providing and ensuring a high quality service, and these costs are designated as quality costs. In order to understand the economic impact that quality costs have on the financial position of a bank and how they can be used to enhance that position, it is crucial that quality costs be defined,

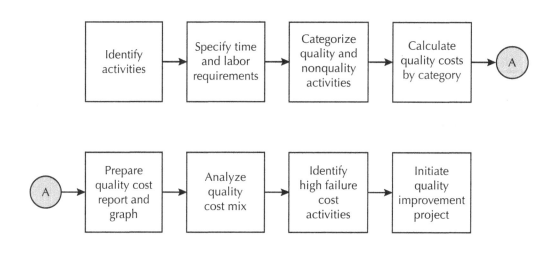

Figure 6.1   The Banc One quality improvement process.

measured, analyzed, and managed. The four quality cost categories of prevention, appraisal, internal failure, and external failure as they relate to the banking industry are defined as follows:

- *Prevention.* Prevention costs are proactive activities that are accomplished before or during processing or service delivery. Prevention costs are those costs associated with operations or activities that keep failure from happening and keep appraisal costs to a minimum. Examples of prevention activities are: new product review, quality planning, quality improvement team meetings, training programs, written policies and procedures, analysis of quality information, and quality information/ improvement projects.

- *Appraisal.* Appraisal costs are those costs incurred to project or predict quality levels and to ascertain the condition of a product or service in order to determine its degree of conformance to quality standards or specifications. Examples of appraisal activities are: inspection of incoming work, supplies, and material; periodic inspection of work-in-process; and checking, balancing, verifying, final inspection, shopper surveys, customer surveys, focus groups, and analysis of customer correspondence/complaints.

- *Internal failure.* Internal failure costs are those costs incurred to correct service or products not conforming to standards or specifications *prior to* delivery to the customer. Examples of internal failure are: machine downtime, scrap and waste due to improperly processed forms or reports, and rework of incorrectly processed work.

- *External failure.* External failure costs are those costs incurred as a result of correcting service or products not conforming to standard or specifications *after* delivery to the customer or correcting a product or service that the customer perceives does not conform to specified standard. Examples of external failure costs are: investigation time, payment of interest penalties, reprocessing of an item, scrap due to improperly processed or incorrect forms or reports, time spent with disgruntled customers, and lost or never acquired business resulting from a poor service quality reputation.

Most appraisal and all failure costs were considered the "cost of poor quality." These costs would disappear if the product or service were defect free and conformed to standards and specifications during or at the time of completion or delivery.

When the four categories of quality costs are added together they are called total quality costs for a product, function, or service. In aggregate, these costs range from 10% to 30% of sales and from 25% to 40% of operating expense. The latter is the way quality costs are measured in banks, which do not have sales. This range has been verified in banking time and time again. It represents a tremendous opportunity to reduce cost and increase customer satisfaction.

Objective

The objective of a quality cost measurement is to aid a company in determining by function, by product or product line, where the highest costs of quality are so improvement efforts can be targeted there. The goal should be to improve quality, productivity, and profitability by reducing quality costs. Revenue can also be increased by increasing customer satisfaction, which results in increased loyalty and repurchase.

The quantitative data from quality cost measurement supply management with necessary information so that it can optimize quality improvement resource allocation. High appraisal and failure costs alert management to problems that may have been previously overlooked. As a result, improvement projects can be undertaken to reduce cost and improve quality, productivity, and profitability. A companywide program alerts employees to the emphasis being placed on quality and their responsibility to meet the company's quality objectives. The companywide commitment to quality increases productivity, since work done right the first time need not be redone. Further, increased productivity and higher profitability and customer satisfaction should give the company a better position in the competitive marketplace.

Getting Started

The company's specific objective will determine how the process is to be implemented. However, there are basic guidelines to follow when implementing quality cost measurement:

- Start small.

- Do not attempt to quality cost every product or service or function within the company.

- Start with activities that you suspect may have high failure or appraisal costs.

Once you have selected the area to be measured, begin data collection.

First, develop a complete list of all operations, activities, and jobs in order to estimate costs based upon actual operating activity and expense. The list details each task or operation performed in the area and the time spent performing each task. Prevention activities and time spent performing them are included on this list since they are part of total quality costs. Then develop a flowchart to assure that all activities are captured and to balance labor activities and costs. Time can be allocated as a percentage of total available labor time or directly as total hours spent (recommended). Total hours spent performing all tasks should equal total labor hours available in the area. In either case, the total number of labor hours available in an area must be ascertained and specified, along with the average salary level of employees. Categorize each activity a quality activity (in one of the four categories) or a non quality (production) activity. Once quality activities, salary level, and time spent performing the activities have been specified, quality costs can be calculated by multiplying the labor time for each activity by the average salary level.

Analyze the expense statement to determine whether any other direct expenses are quality cost items. If so, assign them to a specific quality cost category.

Examples of other direct expenses are:

- Internal or external training expenses charged (prevention)

- The purchase or maintenance of test equipment (appraisal)

- Destruction of forms (internal failure)

- Interest penalties or income lost due to poor quality (external failure)

List the activities and their related costs, by category, on the quality cost report and total it (see Figure 6.2). Only those activities that fall into the four categories are listed. Then identify the largest single opportunities of appraisal and failure. High appraisal costs are signs of possible improvement opportunities that can be reduced with proper prevention. If it's not practical to start all efforts immediately, develop a Pareto diagram using this data to determine which project to undertake first (see Figures 6.3 and 6.4).

Operation	Prevention	Appraisal	Internal Failure	External Failure	Total
Making a Loan					
Run a credit check	$ 0.00	$ 0.00	$ 26.13	$ 0.00	$ 26.13
Prepare and put through GL tickets and I/L input sheets	0.00	0.00	248.19	0.00	248.19
Review documents	0.00	3,013.78	7.84	0.00	3,021.62
Make document corrections, gather additional documents or information	0.00	0.00	1,013.65	0.00	1,013.65
Prepare tickler file, review and follow up on titles, insurance, 2nd meetings, and UCC's	0.00	156.75	0.00	0.00	156.75
Review all output	0.00	2,244.14	0.00	0.00	2,244.14
Correct rejects and incorrect output	0.00	0.00	425.84	0.00	425.84
Work associated with the incomplete collateral report	0.00	0.00	0.00	78.38	78.38
Work associated with dealer calls dealing with any problems and the time to research and communicate	0.00	0.00	2,481.88	2,481.88	
I/L system downtime	0.00	0.00	519.89	0.00	519.89
Time spent training or being trained on I/L	1,366.34	0.00	0.00	0.00	1,366.34
Loan Payment					
Receive and process payments from all sources	0.00	261.25	783.75	0.00	1,045.00
Respond to inquiries when no coupon is presented with payments	0.00	0.00	783.75	0.00	783.75
Loan Payoff					
Receive and process payoff and release document	0.00	0.00	13.06	0.00	13.06
Research payoff problems	0.00	0.00	13.06	0.00	13.06
Total Cost of Quality	$1,366.34	$5,675.92	$3,835.15	$2,560.25	$13,437.66
Cost of Quality as a % of Total Quality Cost	10.17%	42.24%	28.54%	19.05%	100.00%
Cost of Quality as a % of Reported Salary Expense	2.60%	10.79%	7.29%	4.87%	25.54%

Figure 6.2   Quality cost report—installment loans.

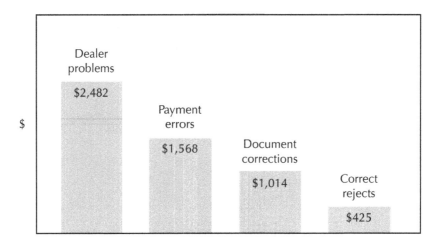

Figure 6.3 Pareto diagram—failures.

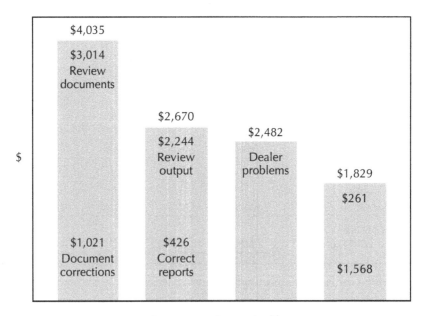

Figure 6.4 Pareto diagram—failure and appraisal improvement opportunities.

The success of a quality improvement project depends on accurate diagnosis and the application of cause-and-effect analysis to the problem. The quality costs data specifies the symptom or effect, but until the causes are known, identified, and tested no action should be taken to correct the problem. To attempt to solve a problem without knowing the cause could increase quality costs and negate the purpose of the quality cost measurement. There are several good root cause analysis techniques that can be used here. Having properly identified the cause or causes of the problem, the team can use the improvement project to set goals and a course of action to correct it. Potential savings based on the proposed course of action can then be estimated. The team can evaluate the success of the improvement project and the quality cost program by measuring the actual shift or reduction in quality costs while also measuring the internal quality level and external customer perceptions. Typical improvement activities yielded as much as 5:1 or even 10:1 return on investment. These 11 quality improvement projects yielded an 8:1 average return.

In addition to the team monitoring quality cost changes effective at the conclusion of the project, continuous measurement should be done to assure the gain has been held.

Relationship of Cost of Poor Quality to Defects and Customer Satisfaction

The results of 11 quality cost measurement studies included quality costs as a percentage of total expense, the overall defect rate from quality standards, the largest individual quality improvement opportunity identified, and the overall measure of customer satisfaction for each department or service. When these measurements were correlated, some interesting relationships were exposed. Low poor quality cost as a percent of total quality costs predicts a small opportunity for improvement. Conversely, a high percentage usually predicts a large opportunity for improvement.

When defect rates are not correlated to improvement opportunities, neither high nor low defect rates predict improvement opportunities of the same relative size. In fact, a low defect rate can often hide large individual improvement opportunities.

The data in this study showed that where large individual quality cost opportunities exist there is a less than acceptable customer perception of the service level provided. Therefore, defect rates are not very useful in identifying or predicting the level of quality cost improvement opportunities.

Customer survey results may be a better indicator as to which areas will benefit from quality cost measurement and improvement team efforts. Once the problem has been identified and improved, not only will the cost savings be realized, but there is likely to be a direct and positive impact on customer satisfaction and retention. Satisfaction increases lead to greater loyalty and repurchases, which lead to greater revenue, lower costs, and significantly increased profitability.

EDUCATION

Using Cost of Quality in a University Environment

In 1992 the University of Western Ontario formed a quality center to drive quality and productivity improvement within the university. Their early efforts with process improvement teams were not as successful as management had hoped. One of the major areas that had not been addressed was an effective means of measuring the opportunity for the teams and of measuring the savings to be realized by the improvements recommended.

Cost of quality (COQ) had been used very effectively by manufacturing organizations for many years to identify opportunities and track improvements. With the service sector's increased interest in quality improvement, COQ has also been used as a measurement tool for their projects. It was felt that COQ had excellent potential in a university environment as well.

The manager of financial systems in the department of finance was convinced of the value of COQ as an effective quality improvement measurement tool. He volunteered his department and identified two pilot projects, major equipment replacement and telephone system review. A project facilitator/trainer was assigned.

The major concern was to ensure that the application of COQ would be viewed as a "management tool" rather than a "financial tool." As a management tool, COQ would enable the process improvement teams to manage their improvement efforts; as a financial tool, it could be seen as just another method to monitor the employees.

For the pilot projects to be successful, it was necessary that the approach and methodology be seen as equally important as the COQ measurement tool (see Figure 6.5). Team members were given extensive training that consisted of a disciplined approach to process improvement. An integrated process improvement and potential problem solving model was used, supported by appropriate quality tools. In addition to cost of quality, these included brainstorming, process mapping, and the seven basic quality tools: Pareto diagram, check sheet, cause-and-effect diagram, scatter diagram, histogram, control chart, and run chart.

Another key factor in the success of the pilot projects was management's role in the support and guidance of the improvement teams. One of the most significant challenges faced by the management team was to free up time for the improvement team members to work on their projects. The team members spent 25% of their time on their projects. This meant that part of their daily work had to be off loaded or delayed. Some areas were more successful than others in reassigning work. It was essential that the teams see quality improvement as part of their job and not something else to be added to their duties. The key role of management was to monitor progress by focusing on the activities or steps of the team's process and note the results of team efforts. By ensuring the team followed all the appropriate steps, the results would follow.

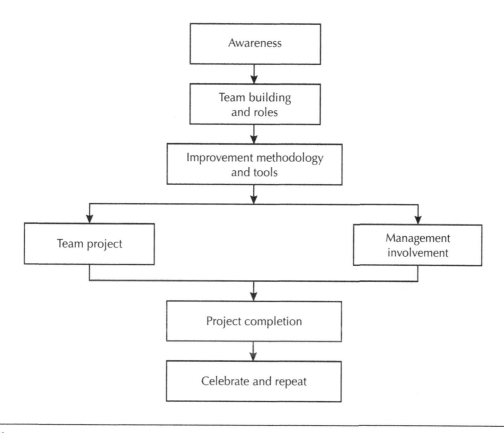

Figure 6.5 Process improvement team methodology.

Major Equipment Replacement Project

The purpose of this first project was to develop a process within the finance department for equipment replacement. Equipment included personal computers, copiers, and facsimile, microfiche, and microfilm machines. The project would address individual needs assessment, training, and communication. The team consisted of six members from the finance department.

The team initially documented and flowcharted the current equipment replacement process. They found that the decision to replace equipment was being made by one individual using an informal process based on the best assessment of need. The team then conducted customer focus group meetings to gather information on perceptions of the current process. They found a lack of communication with staff members on the current equipment replacement process and the nonexistence of a feedback mechanism to notify individuals when a request for equipment was not approved. The perception was that the current method was not objective. In many cases, input from the individuals requesting the equipment was not considered.

The team then surveyed a sample of members of the finance department to determine the level of equipment and training satisfaction. Using the information collected, the team was able to estimate the cost of quality for the existing process. The results of this data are shown in Figure 6.6. They based an estimate of loss in productivity on the level of dissatisfaction expressed by those surveyed. They determined the number of individuals using each type of equipment. As a result, it was possible to calculate the annual COQ by multiplying the number of individuals times hours per year times an average hourly salary rate of $28. The annual COQ for equipment was approximately $210,000. They also calculated the COQ for computer training to be approximately $145,000, bringing the total annual COQ to almost $355,000.

The team then developed an equipment replacement process using a team approach. This included annual budget preparation, repairs, reserve appropriations, and computer training to be centralized within the department of finance. They then presented management with a list of seven recommendations complete with implementation costs (see Figure 6.7).

Result. The recommendations had a onetime cost of approximately $2,200 and an annual cost of approximately $12,500. The savings represented a payback period of less than one month!

Telephone System Review Project

The purpose of this second project was to review the existing telephone system and make recommendations for improvement to maximize customer satisfaction in a cost-effective manner. Six members of the finance department volunteered to participate on this project.

The team developed a telephone system review checklist to better understand the number and types of calls being made to the department. Next the team conducted a customer focus group to determine the problems that were being experienced by individuals contacting the department. The most frequent problems identified were:

1. Transfer of calls to the wrong area

2. Incomplete messages received

3. a. Picking same phone

   b. Picking same phone with disconnect

4. Lack of notification when leaving the office

5. Expert not available when immediate help needed

6. Inexperienced or temporary help answering calls

7. General calls routed to director of finance

8. Available options unused

9. Clearing of voice-mail box by secretary

Description	(a) Total Replies	(a) Weighted Average of Satisfaction Level (10=max)	(b) Weighted Average Level of Dissatisfaction	(b) Estimated Productivity Loss	(c) Finance Total Staff	(d) Estimated % of Staff Involved	(e) Weekly Average Hours Used	Weeks Per Year	(f) Average Hourly Salary	Estimated Annual Cost of Quality
Personal computer	17	7.3	2.7	27% ×	45 ×	89% ×	10 ×	46 ×	$28 =	$140,324
Copiers	19	7.1	2.9	29% ×	45 ×	100% ×	2 ×	46 ×	$28 =	34,166
Fax	17	5.4	4.6	46% ×	45 ×	89% ×	1 ×	46 ×	$28 =	23,661
Microfiche	10	5.8	4.2	42% ×	45 ×	53% ×	0.3 ×	46 ×	$28 =	3,644
Microfilm	10	4.0	6.0	60% ×	45 ×	53% ×	0.4 ×	46 ×	$28 =	7,321
Estimated cost of quality for equipment										$209,316
Computer Training (g)	19	7.5	2.5	25% ×	45 ×	100% ×	10 ×	46 ×	$28 =	144,900
Estimated cost of quality for equipment and training										$354,216

Notes:

(a) These schedules are based on the survey of 19 members in the department.

(b) A satisfaction level of 10 (100%) indicated full productivity. A satisfaction level of 7 indicated a 70% level of productivity and a corresponding 30% loss in productivity.

(c) Approximate number of non-managerial staff in the department of finance.

(d) Estimated percentage of staff involved is the number of responses divided by the sample size (e.g., 17/19 = 89%)

(e) Average weekly hours that equipment is used was determined by the survey.

(f) Average hourly salary for non-managerial staff is estimated at $28.

(g) When asked, only two people surveyed said they felt they had been adequately trained to perform computer related functions. On a weighted average basis, staff in the survey felt that they were 75% trained to use their computers. Accordingly, lack of training is estimated to reduce personal computer productivity usage by 25%.

Figure 6.6 Finance department costs of quality for equipment and training.

Cost Considerations, Department of Finance, Equipment and Training

Start up costs		
Initial assessment of inventory and training	50 hours @$28 =	$1,400
Data base design	14 hours @ $33 =	462
Data base approval	4 people @ 2 hours @$44 =	352
		$2,214
Annual costs		
Annual time for team meetings	12 meetings @ 3 hours for 3 people @ $33 =	$3,564
Ongoing support time for team meetings	12 meetings @ 3 hours for 3 people @ $33 =	3,564
Maintenance of inventory	1 hour per month @ $33 =	396
Communications time	7 hours per month for 1 person @ $33 =	2,772
Estimated annual costs		$10,296
Total estimated costs for implementation		**$12,510**
Average hourly salaries: *Non-managerial $28/hr* *PMA $33/hr* *Managerial $44/hr*		

Figure 6.7 Estimated implementation costs.

The team then summarized the cost of quality for the current process (Figure 6.8). They first determined the time it would take to correct the problem for each of the first seven problem types. For example, time wasted by calls transferred to the wrong area was 6.5 minutes. For the last two problems, paying for options not used and clearing phone mail, they calculated the cost of each. Clearing phone mail varied from department to department, depending on who was involved and the number of messages. Based on the information collected through the checklist, they then calculated the COQ for each type of problem. These varied in cost from area to area depending on frequency of errors. The total COQ for the telephone systems review project was approximately $65,500 per year.

The team then developed an employee telephone survey to solicit suggestions for improvement. Using input from their customers, the team developed recommendations in 11 areas. The cost of quality was recalculated based on these recommendations (Figure 6.9).

	FABA*	Gen. Acct.	Audit	Fees	Research	General	Total
1. Transfer call to wrong area—6.5 min.		7/day $4,447.63	1/week $190.61	10/day $6,353.75			$10,991.99
2. Message not complete—6.5 min.						1/day 635.38	635.38
3. a. Picking same phone—6.5 min.		3/day 1,906.13	5/day 4,765.31	6/day 3,812.25			10,483.69
b. Picking same phone with disconnect—8 min.		4/day 3,128.00		2/day 1,564.00			4,692.00
4. Not telling someone when leaving office —6.5 min.	8/day 7,624.50						
—10 min.		3/day 2,932.50		2/day 1,955.00	3/day 2,932.50		7,820.00
—13 min.					1/day 1,270.75		1,270.75
5. Person needs immediate help—expert not there (e.g., student awards, systems problem)—15 min.	1/day 2,199.38	1/day 1,466.25	6/week 2,639.25	2/day 2,932.50			9,237.38
6. Inexperienced or temp. help—5 min.						160 days 1st month 1/person (8) 306.67	306.67
7. General calls going to director—10 min						4/week 1,564.00	1,564.00
8. Having options not used—paying for options not activated						660.24	660.24
9. Clearing the phone mail box	6,524.81	1,466.25	2,199.38				10,190.44
						TOTAL	$65,477.02

5 days, 51 weeks, 0.383333 Staff (23/hr), 0.575 PMA ($34.5/hr), 0.766666 Sen. PMA ($46/hr)
* FABA = Financial Analysis and Budget Administration

Figure 6.8 Finance department cost of quality—*before* telephone system review.

	FABA*	Gen. Acct.	Audit	Fees	Research	General	Total
1. Transfer call to wrong area—0 min.		7/day 0.00	1/week 0.00	10/day 0.00			$ 0.00
2. Message not complete—0.5 min.						1/day 48.88	48.88
3. a. Picking same phone—0 min.		3/day 0.00	5/day 0.00	6/day 0.00			0.00
b. Picking same phone with disconnect—0 min.		4/day 0.00		2/day 0.00			0.00
4. Not telling someone when leaving office —2.5 min.	8/day 2,932.50						2,932.50
—2.5 min.		3/day 733.13		2/day 488.75	3/day 733.13		1,955.00
—2.5 min.					1/day 244.38		244.38
5. Person needs immediate help—expert not there (e.g., student awards, systems problem)—2.5 min.	1/day 366.56	1/day 244.38	6/week 439.88	2/day 488.75			1,539.56
6. Inexperienced or temp. help—0 min.	160 days, 1st month, 1 call/person (8 new people)—0.00						0.00
7. General calls going to director—0 min.						4/week 0.00	0.00
8. Having options not used—paying for options not activated						0.00	0.00
9. Clearing the phone mail box	4,985.25	1,466.25	2,639.25				10,557.00
10. Training—1 hour						25@$23 21@$34.50 6@$46	1,575.50
						TOTAL	$18,852.81

* FABA = Financial Analysis and Budget Administration

Figure 6.9   Finance department cost of quality—*after* telephone system review.

Result. The COQ after implementation of the recommendations would be about $18,900 per year. Part of the new COQ included approximately $1,600 for training. This project resulted in an annual savings of about $46,600.

Conclusion

These two pilot projects clearly demonstrated that cost of quality is an excellent management tool. It was shown that COQ can be used effectively to identify opportunities and track improvements not only in manufacturing and service sectors, but also in the university community.

SOFTWARE DEVELOPMENT—COST OF SOFTWARE QUALITY (COSQ) AT RAYTHEON'S ELECTRONIC SYSTEMS (RES) GROUP

Overview

There are number of success stories about organizations that have successfully applied preventive and appraisal activities to reduce losses due to failure costs and realize tangible gains. In addition to Raytheon, successful organizations include the following:

- Chase Financial Services addressed the joint problems of excess demand and inadequate return on investment (ROI) with an approach that permitted them to improve how the value was delivered and improve ROI.

- JP Morgan Chase & Co. took a measured approach to achieving quality through attention to detail and continuous improvement. This allowed the organization to exceed its total cost of ownership savings objective by 100%.

- Seagate's IT system booked direct savings of approximately $4.5 million overall from quality initiatives.

- Satyam deployed quality practices across 300 individual projects, realizing an annual benefit of $11 million through enterprise-wide deployment.

- Hughes BPO realized a significant improvement in customer satisfaction measures, going from 62% to 87%.

- Microsoft leveraged its own technology to complete more than 200 quality cost projects and deliver more than $30 million to the bottom line over a three-year period.

Measurement of Value

The cost of software quality (CoSQ) initiative must take a practical view of how value is measured. If different stakeholders do not share consistent interpretations on the value of the work performed, the benefit-to-cost ratio (BCR) will be skewed and challenged. However, it is important not to confuse benefit-to-cost ratio with return on investment; benefit-to-cost reflects the initial gain, while ROI establishes the expectation of benefit over the long term.

It can be summarized that any source from which ROI calculations will be derived must be defensible and stand up to challenge. Estimates should be from credible sources and in cases of ambiguity, the conservative interpretation should be applied. Where possible, the effects of a project should be isolated so that savings are not attributed to external or uncontrollable factors. Whatever methodology is used, it should be communicated to all stakeholders for transparency and accountability.

Cost Drivers

According to documented studies conducted by Capers Jones, the most effective method for measuring the economic value of quality in software is to analyze the total cost of ownership (TCO) for applications. This mitigates the variation between different technologies and programming languages to avoid having false indicators prompt incorrect or contradictory responses. The costs are affected by prominent areas of waste or expense, termed by Dr. Jones as "cost drivers." The most prominent and frequent are listed here:

- Finding and fixing defects
- Project interruption or cancellation
- Documentation (beyond base technical information)
- Vulnerability to and recovery from security attacks
- Changes to requirements during development
- Complexity of technical solutions (i.e., programming, coding, object analysis)
- Ongoing customer support
- Meetings, communication, and management activities

The hypothesis is that taking steps to reduce the cost drivers with additional preventive or control measures will reduce the effect of the cost drivers, subsequently reducing the overall cost of software quality.

Case Study Introduction

The intent of this case study is to provide visibility into a benchmark software development organization that currently uses CoSQ to document the results of improvement programs and to observe how CoSQ concepts relate to the consistent production of high quality software. The RES organization was chosen as a case study subject because, using a CoSQ approach, they were able to show specific, measured benefits from their software improvement efforts. Moreover, they collected data and lessons learned about their CoSQ implementation activities. See the discussion of RES CoSQ activities in Chapter 4 in the section on software quality costs.

Although RES is in the contract systems business, they are similar in many ways to the commercial software supplier who wants to achieve a successful and profitable business by satisfying customers with a high quality software (or system) product delivered on time and within budget.

Although there are many reasons to use CoQ in an organization, RES used it to measure and demonstrate the effects of their ongoing software improvement program. Specifically, CoSQ was used to show the costs and benefits of their investments over the chronology of their improvement program. This is a good example of the way in which a few leading organizations are using CoSQ today.

RES and Its Improvement Program

Raytheon Electronic Systems (previously the Raytheon Equipment Division) builds real-time, mission critical, embedded software systems under contract to defense and commercial customers. They build these systems in the domains of air traffic control, vessel traffic management, digital communications, ground and shipboard radar, satellite communications, undersea warfare, military command and control, and combat training. The systems they build are large and typically range in size from 70–500 KDSI (1,000 delivered source instructions).

Since 1988 RES has been engaged in a software improvement initiative driven by the need to prevent overrunning schedules and budgets and the crisis-driven environment that resulted. Once budgets and schedules came under some control, they turned their attention to the goal of reducing rework.

The RES improvement initiative affected roughly 350–600 professionals. The investment for the initiative has been steady at about $1 million per year. The SEI CMMI-based approach was later adopted and used to help focus their improvements. Following this approach, they were self-assessed at CMMI Level 1 in 1988, at Level 2 in 1990, at Level 3 in 1992, and as of 1995 operate all new projects starting at Level 4. (For a description of the SEI CMMI levels, see Figure 4.4 in the Software Quality Costs section of Chapter 4.) In 1995, RES won the coveted IEEE Computer Society/Software Engineering Institute Software Process Achievement (SPA) Award.

Their improvement program strategy included a dual focus on product and process. The product focal point areas included system definition, requirements definition, inspections and integration, and qualification testing. The process focal point areas included development planning and management controls, training, and pathfinding.

Cost of Software Quality (CoSQ)

CoSQ was chosen as one of four measures to track because it provided a framework to determine rework levels as well as the overall return on investment (ROI) of their improvement program. The other measures chosen were software productivity, cost performance index, and overall product quality.

The following describes how RES used CoSQ as a method for tracking rework and calculating ROI in their software improvement program. It is adapted from previously published sources.

The RES CoSQ Model. Cost of software quality (CoSQ) was considered the sum of two components: the cost of non-conformance (rework costs) and the cost of conformance (prevention and appraisal costs). RES determined that they needed to track these quality cost categories. The model shown in Figure 6.10 was used to accumulate them.

In this model, CoSQ is the sum of the costs of appraisal, prevention, and rework. The focus on rework is important because it represents the major component of waste and scrap of software development. One of the most costly activities in software development today is reworking or redoing what has already been done. There are many underlying reasons for this, but most scrap and rework are the result of flawed requirements, changing conditions, and unexpected problems. For some reason, software professionals have come to accept mountains of rework as part of their everyday activities—in some cases, they do not think of it as rework. For example, precious schedule time is spent on fixes for code defects when software doesn't perform as expected, or on redesign of a user interface because the customer expects something different from what is provided. Many software engineers think of this as the natural way things are meant to happen.

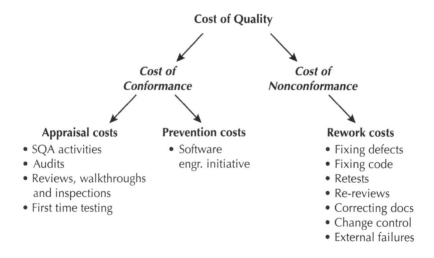

Figure 6.10 The RES CoSQ model.

The definitions of each sub-category, which were brief for reasons of simplicity, were subject to misinterpretation. This was addressed by refining the definitions as experience was gained in using them. This required five iterations of the initial data gathering exercise before a satisfactory level of consistency of definition was obtained.

Breaking these basic quality cost categories (rework, appraisal, and prevention) into subcategories, defining the subcategories, and assigning project activities and costs to them proved to be a difficult task for RES because the existing work breakdown structure used on the software projects did not correspond well to the CoSQ categories.

CoSQ Data Gathering. Project costs were collected using the conventional work breakdown structure, and project leads periodically would manually reassign all costs to the cost of quality subcategories. Project CoSQ data were then combined. Improvement initiative costs were factored in as a separate prevention project. These were then used to produce the organizational CoSQ average and trend data.

In the long term, RES wanted to develop a common work breakdown structure to provide as close a mapping to the cost of quality as possible. This would also entail a revision of the cost accounting system and possibly the time card reporting system as well.

Experiences and Lessons Learned

CoSQ Model Usage Lessons. RES encountered a number of experiences using the CoSQ model. Many questions arose about how to allocate costs to subcategories. There was variation in the methods used to break down the actual costs to the defined cost bin. This was resolved by refining the subcategory definitions and by analyzing and comparing the sub-allocation algorithms employed by the six target project leaders.

It was necessary to have the project leader generate the data rather than an administrator because the project leader possessed firsthand knowledge of project particulars as well as good engineering judgment.

Using CoSQ Data to Understand the Impact of Improvement. Table 6.1 shows how the CoSQ data were used by RES to track the impact of their improvement program over the years. Starting at CMMI Level 1 in 1988, RES introduced their software process improvement (SPI) program. Using the results tracked in 15 projects, they achieved CMMI Level 3 practices in a little over three years. As seen in Figure 6.11, at the Level 1 stage, the RES CoSQ fluctuated between 55% and 67% of total project costs and by the time of reaching Level 3 process maturity, their CoSQ had dropped to approximately 40% of total project cost. In 1990 when RES was approaching CMMI Level 3, total CoSQ was about 45% of total project costs and its ratio of conformance to nonconformance costs was approximately 1.5. In 1994, when RES was adopting a goal of CMMI Level 4, total CoSQ was about 24% of total project costs and its ratio of conformance to nonconformance costs was approximately 3.0.

Table 6.1 CoSQ tracking at specific points in time.

	Performance	Rework (Nonconformance)	Appraisal (Conformance)	Prevention
1988	34%	44%	15%	7%
1990	55%	18%	15%	12%
1992	66%	11%	– 23% –	
1994	76%	6%	– 18% –	

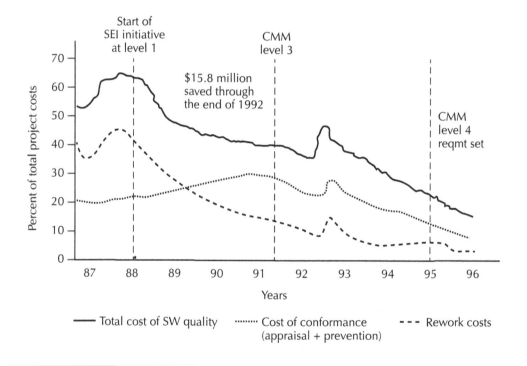

Figure 6.11 Tracking the cost of software quality at RES.

Rework Cost Savings. Figure 6.11 also shows the trend in the average cost of rework from the start of the improvement initiative. In the two years prior to the initiative, the rework costs had averaged about 41% of total project costs. In the two years following, that value had dropped to about 20% and the trend was continuing downward. In 1995, CoSQ was approximately 25% of total project costs and the rework due to both internal and external failures had been reduced to about 6% of total project costs.

Rework savings were achieved at the expense of a small increase in appraisal or prevention costs. For example, appraisal costs rose when informal reviews were replaced by formal inspections and prevention costs rose when inspection training was instituted. Also, rework costs associated with fixing defects found during design rose from about 0.75% to about 2% of project cost and those associated with fixing defects found during coding rose from about 2.5% to about 4% of project cost.

The major reduction in rework costs was that associated with fixing source code problems found during integration, which dropped to about 20% of its original value. The second largest contributor to the rework reduction was the cost of re-testing, which decreased to about half its initial value. This clearly indicates that the additional costs of performing formal inspections and the training that must precede it are justified on the basis of finding problems earlier in the process, resulting in a more efficient integration.

Software Quality. The ultimate measure of quality is the contribution that software has made to RES success with software intensive systems. Improvements made have enabled success on several major software intensive programs and have allowed RES to tackle larger software projects. This was concretely demonstrated on several complex system projects by removing software from the critical path and delivering early, thus earning incentives. The primary quantitative measure that RES uses to assess overall product quality is the defect density in the final software products. This density factor is measured as the number of software trouble reports (STR) per 1,000 lines of delivered source instructions (KDSI) on each project. The project densities are combined to compute a monthly weighted average to yield a time-variant plot of the trend. As shown in Figure 6.12, the average level of quality improved from about 17.2 STRs/KDSI to about 4 STRs/KDSI, about a four-time improvement.

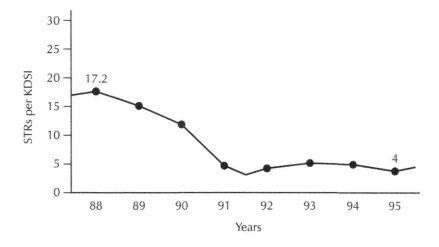

Figure 6.12   Tracking the level of software quality at RES.

Productivity. Data were collected from individual productivity projects in terms of equivalent delivered source instructions (EDSI) per man-month of development effort. The data were combined from all projects using a weighting function and the results showed the average productivity was, in fact, increasing as a function of time—meaning that jobs were costing less. Overall, RES achieved a 170% increase in software productivity as measured on 24 projects over seven years.

Predictability. Management needed to be reassured that the improved productivity figures were being used to bid new jobs. This issue was addressed by collecting CPI data on the project's budgeted (predicted) cost and actual cost at completion (CAC). This cost performance index ratio (CAC/budget) for each project was then used to compute the monthly weighted average (using the same approach as the cost of quality) to yield a plot of this time-variant measure. The results were encouraging, showing that the cost performance index was improved dramatically from about the 20% overrun range prior to the start of the initiative to the 1%–2% range by early 1993. Overall, their cost performance index (CAC/budget) went from about 1.43 to 1.00 in the first three years, and has been steady at about 1.00 since.

Other ROI Results. RES has won additional business based on process maturity results (no amount reported). Software personnel work less overtime than before and this has led to lower turnover rates. The overall payoff of their improvement program is reported to be 7.5 times (not including a $9.6 million schedule incentive award in '91). For example, in 1990 they spent $1.1M on improvements and determined that the cost of nonconformance was reduced by $8.2M in that year. Other leading organizations have realized similar bottom line benefits[1].

CoSQ Costs and Benefits. CoSQ analysis cost RES about $25K of overhead for the first-time exercise. They repeated the CoSQ analysis exercise about a year later and added the analysis process to the normal senior management process reviews on a semi-annual basis.

The CoSQ analysis used by RES was determined to be a viable mechanism for measuring the overall effect of software process improvement. It can be used to isolate software waste/scrap as part of an attempt to drive it to zero. The information learned in applying the approach benefited the projects involved in the analysis by providing early feedback. The improvement of the organization's standard process was also facilitated.

Institutionalization of CoSQ Tracking. By 1993, after three years, the data gathering exercise for CoSQ had become routine. Although the full analysis was being made semi-annually, some department managers were requiring their project leaders to provide the CoSQ data along with their normal monthly tracking data. In retrospect, more emphasis could have been placed on transitioning to a common work breakdown structure geared to the collection of CoSQ.

Case Study Implications

Because the RES use of the CoSQ approach was pioneering, the company learned many lessons that others will not have to learn the hard way. CoSQ was primarily used as an after-the-fact measure of their SPI program's cost and benefits, rather than as a tool to guide their SPI program (which was the CMMI). It is expected that other organizations using the CMM approach to SPI will want to do likewise. A detailed analysis of the CMMI versus CoSQ will be needed, so that investment opportunities can be better focused on high impact areas. This analysis should be focused on the impact of prevention activities in the 18 CMM key process areas on internal and externally induced rework.

RES encountered specific difficulties in the following areas:

- When and how the CoSQ data were gathered, analyzed, reported, and used

- How the model clashed with other models that were already in use

- The lack of an existing WBS with well defined categories that correspond easily to CoSQ

- How the model was defined at the detailed levels

- How the model was implemented in the organization

- How CoSQ was used for root cause analysis

- How the model was used to stimulate SPI and quality improvements

These difficulties can be overcome with appropriate training and coaching.

RES's use of CoSQ occurred within the context of its contract-oriented systems business, and therefore the CoSQ approach was adapted to the specifics of that situation. It will likely be necessary to modify a more general approach for use in other situations, with different business success parameters. These situations include:

- Standard product-oriented businesses

- Service delivery situations

- Technology-based startups

End Note

1. Krasner, H. *Accumulating the Body of Evidence for the Payoff of SPI—1997,* see www.utexas.edu/coe/cqi/archive.

Appendix A
Basic Financial Concepts

To understand the relationship of quality costs to company cost accounting systems, it is best to start with a conventional cost structure (Figure A.1). An explanation of this normal distribution of costs follows.

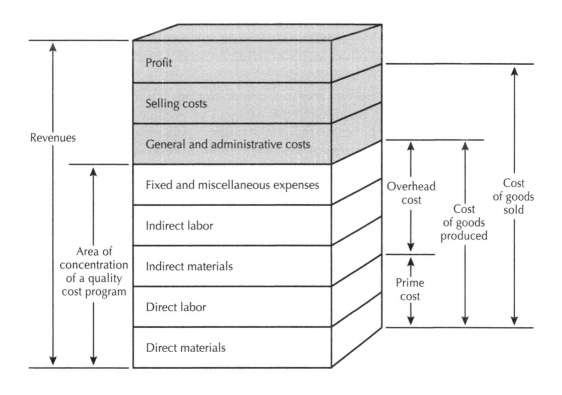

Figure A.1 Conventional cost and price structures.

PRIME COSTS

Prime costs, consisting of two parts, are the basic or standard costs of product manufacture or service operations:

1. *Direct materials.* Raw materials, semi-finished products, and finished product. Supplies such as printing inks, coolants, gloves, and cutting tools used in the operation of the business but not built into the end product, are not considered direct materials.

2. *Direct labor.* Labor applied to convert direct materials or other input into the finished product. These costs can be specifically identified with basic product manufacturing or service operations. Examples include wages and related costs of workers who assemble inputs into finished goods, who operate equipment integral to the production process, or who deal directly with customers in delivering a service.

OVERHEAD COSTS

Overhead costs are all costs incurred in direct support of prime costs, that is, in direct support of product manufacturing or service operations. Overhead has three parts:

1. *Indirect materials.* Supplies consumed in operations but not directly a part of the end product. Included in this category of overhead costs are items such as protective boxes for material handling, packaging supplies, perishable tools, clerical supplies, and communication costs.

2. *Indirect labor.* Wages and salaries earned by employees who do not work directly on the end product or service but whose services are related to the production process or service provided. Included in this category are supervisors, operations support engineers and technicians, material handlers, storeroom personnel, and janitors.

3. *Fixed and miscellaneous expenses.* Depreciation, taxes, rent, warranties, and insurance on the assets used in operations are included in this category.

COST OF GOODS PRODUCED

The cost of goods produced, the basic or standard cost of product manufacturing or service operations, is the total of prime costs and overhead costs.

COST OF GOODS SOLD

To arrive at the total cost to a company of the delivery of products or services to customers, two additional areas of cost must be added to the cost of goods produced.

1. *Selling costs.* Those costs incurred in an effort to achieve sales and in transferring the completed product or service to the customer. In addition to direct sales costs, categories include marketing, advertising, warehousing, billing, and transportation.

2. *General and administrative (G&A) costs.* A catchall classification for all other business-incurred costs. Categories generally include financial, personnel, legal, public relations, and information systems.

REVENUES AND PROFIT

The last rung in the conventional cost structure is pretax profit, which is simply the difference between revenues and cost of goods sold.

We can now look at the conventional cost structure in relation to a quality cost program. A significant portion of the costs defined in the quality cost system will appear in the cost of goods produced: direct materials, direct labor, indirect materials, indirect labor, and fixed and miscellaneous expenses. It should be clear that any reduction in the cost of quality has a positive effect on profit.

The full significance of quality cost reductions can be appreciated when it is realized that some larger quality cost problems affect costs in all five categories of the cost of goods produced. In smaller firms or when the quality cost problem is sufficiently large, even general and administrative costs are affected.

MECHANICS OF QUALITY COST COLLECTION

The method of accumulating costs in a medium or larger organization requires some basic segregation within the conventional cost structure. Often called a "chart of accounts," it defines in greater detail the costs incurred in the total operation. The number of accounts and their descriptions vary from company to company. Each firm's chart of accounts is developed to suit the needs of that particular concern. A significant portion of the costs in a quality cost program are already identified as a result of previous requirements for other purposes and some details can be found in the chart of accounts. Generally, job orders, work orders, or other similar systems are used to further define costs within the numbered accounts in the chart of accounts.

A quality cost program identifies a portion of the financial structure in a slightly different manner than conventional financial methods. It concentrates in areas where expenses are necessary because the organization is not able to operate at 100% performance to standard. When possible, it is useful to keep the same nomenclature for quality costs similar to the rest of the cost accounting system. Use existing account descriptions from the chart of accounts, existing unit or department names, existing product line names, and any other source of terminology that will contribute to the understanding of quality performance throughout the company. This is not creative writing; it is intended to make relationships clear.

The conventional accounting cycle and costing procedure begin with the recording of original business transactions and proceeds to the final preparation and summarizing of balance sheets and profit and loss (P&L) statements. As daily business transactions occur, they are recorded in a journal. The typical business makes use of many types of journals including cash, sales, purchase, and general. The ledger is the next step. Journal entries are *posted* to the ledger. Annually, quarterly, or monthly, the financial condition of the firm is stated on the balance sheet and the results of the operation are stated on the P&L statement. These are prepared from ledger accounts. The balance sheet shows the financial health of the business at a particular date, while the P&L statement is a record of the financial gain or loss during a period of time.

GENERAL ACCOUNTING PRACTICES

The rules and conventions of accounting are commonly referred to as principles. The term *principle* is used here to mean "a general law or rule adopted as a guide to action; a settled ground rule or basis of conduct or practice." This definition describes a principle as a general law or rule to be used as a guide to action; accounting principles do not prescribe exactly how each event occurring in a business should be recorded. Consequently, there are a great many activities in the accounting practice that differ from one company to another. Differences reflect the fact that the accountant has considerable latitude within the "generally accepted accounting principles" in which to express his own ideas as to the best way of recording and reporting a specific event.

Accounting principles are man-made. Unlike the principles of mathematics, physics, chemistry, and the other natural sciences, accounting principles were not deduced from basic axioms, nor is their validity verifiable by observation and experiment. Instead, they have evolved by the following process:

1. A problem is recognized

2. Someone works out a solution to this problem

3. As other people agree it is a good solution, its use is gradually accepted

4. It then becomes an accounting principle

Some previously accepted principles fall from favor with the passage of time or changes in technology. This evolutionary process is continuous.

THE BALANCE SHEET

Resources owned by a business are called assets. The claims of various parties against these assets are called equities. There are two types of equities: (1) liabilities, which are the claims of creditors, i.e., everyone other than the owners of the business; and (2) owner's equity, which is the claim of the owners on the business. Since all assets of a business are claimed by someone (either by owners or by some outside party), and since the total of these claims cannot exceed the amount of assets to be claimed, it follows that the sum of assets equals the sum of liabilities. Accounting systems are set up in such a way that a record is made of two aspects of each event that affects these records—changes in assets and changes in equities.

Let's assume someone starts a business by depositing $20,000 of personal funds in a bank account. The dual aspect of this action is that the business now has an asset in the form of $20,000 in cash, and the owner has a claim against this asset of $20,000.

$$\text{Assets (cash) } \$20,000 = \text{Equities (owner's) } \$20,000$$

If the business then borrowed $10,000 from a bank, the financial records would indicate an increase in assets, making the cash amount $30,000 and establishing a claim against this cash in the amount of $10,000. The financial records (balance sheet) would show the following:

Cash	$30,000	Owed to bank	$10,000
		Owner's equity	$20,000
Total assets	$30,000	Total equities	$30,000

Because every event affects both sides of the balance sheet, this is called a *double entry* system.

The practice of listing assets on the left side and equities on the right side of the balance sheet is common in the United States. The right side of the balance sheet may be viewed as a description of the sources of capital with which the company operates, and the left side as a description of the form in which that capital is invested on a specified date.

Assets are valuable resources owned by a business and acquired at a measurable money cost. Liabilities are the claims of outsiders against the business, and the owner's equity section of the balance sheet shows the claims of the owners. The owner's equity increases through earnings (the results of profitable operations) and decreases when earnings are paid out in the form of dividends.

Useful information may be obtained from the analysis of succeeding balance sheets. Comparative balance sheet analysis is the study of the trend of the same items, groups of items, or computed items in two or more balance sheets of the same business enterprise on different dates. Comparative analysis portrays the trends of particular features of a business enterprise such as liquidity and debt/equity ratios.

THE PROFIT AND LOSS STATEMENT

The accounting report that summarizes revenue items, expense items, and the difference between them for an accounting period is called the profit and loss (P&L) statement, or sometimes the income and expense statement. The information on the P&L statement is usually more important than information on the balance sheet because it reports the results of current operations.

Like any accounting report, the P&L statement should be prepared in the form that is best for those who use it at whatever level of detail is required. No one specific format is employed, but the following basic categories of cost are found on most P&L statements:

1. *Sales.* The total invoice price of goods delivered to customers plus cash sales made during the period equals gross sales. The sales value of goods rejected by customers and credit given because goods were not as specified are identified separately and netted out of gross sales to provide actual (net) sales.

2. *Cost of Goods Sold.* This item is described as part of the conventional cost structure. It includes the cost of goods produced, selling costs, and G&A costs.

3. *Gross Profit.* The difference between net sales and cost of goods sold.

4. *Selling Expenses.* The cost of selling the goods produced.

5. *Net Profit.* The difference between gross profit and selling expenses, sometimes called operating profit.

6. *Provisions for Income Tax.* Estimated liability for federal, state, and local income tax.

7. *Net Income.* Net gain or loss, determined by subtracting provisions for income tax from profit before income tax.

The conventional cost structure, previously discussed, relates well to the P&L statement. A quality cost program focuses on the cost of goods produced. Quality cost reductions can increase profits or permit a reduction in price while maintaining a constant profit or increase profit while holding prices constant. The P&L statement will always reflect reduced costs of goods sold with a corresponding increase in gross profit—the essence of quality cost program objectives.

Appendix B

Detailed Description of Quality Cost Elements

For future reference and use, detailed quality cost elements are identified in numerical sequence (see Figure B.1 for summary). Individual elements are not applicable to all businesses. It is up to the reader to determine applicability in each case. This list is not meant to contain every element of quality cost applicable to every business. It is intended to give the reader a general idea of what type of elements are contained within each cost category to help in deciding individual classifications for actual use. If a significant cost exists that fits any part of the general description of the quality cost element, it should be used. In many cases, activities involve personnel from one or more departments. No attempt is made to define appropriate departments since each company is organized differently.

1.0	PREVENTION COSTS		
1.1	Marketing/Customer/User	1.4	Operations (Manufacturing or Service) Prevention Costs
1.1.1	Marketing Research		
1.1.2	Customer/User Perception Surveys/ Clinics	1.4.l	Operations Process Validation
		1.4.2	Operations Quality Planning
1.1.3	Contract/Document Review	1.4.2.1	Design and Development of Quality Measurement Control Equipment
1.2	Product/Service/Design Development		
1.2.1	Design Quality Progress Reviews	1.4.3	Operations Support Quality Planning
1.2.2	Design Support Activities	1.4.4	Operator Quality Education
1.2.3	Product Design Qualification Test	1.4.5	Operator SPC/Process Control
1.2.4	Service Design-Qualification	1.5	Quality Administration
1.2.5	Field Trials	1.5.1	Administrative Salaries
1.3	Purchasing Prevention Costs	1.5.2	Administrative Expenses
1.3.1	Supplier Reviews	1.5.3	Quality Program Planning
1.3.2	Supplier Rating	1.5.4	Quality Performance Reporting
1.3.3	Purchase Order Tech Data Reviews	1.5.5	Quality Education
1.3.4	Supplier Quality Planning	1.5.6	Quality Improvement
		1.5.7	Quality System Audits
		1.6	Other Prevention Costs

Figure B.1   Detailed quality cost element summary.   *(continued)*

2.0	**APPRAISAL COSTS**		
2.1	Purchasing Appraisal Costs	2.2.4	Process Control Measurements
2.1.1	Receiving or Incoming Inspections and Tests	2.2.5	Laboratory Support
2.1.2	Measurement Equipment	2.2.6	Measurement (Inspection and Test) Equipment
2.1.3	Qualification of Supplier Product	2.2.6.1	Depreciation Allowances
2.1.4	Source Inspection and Control Programs	2.2.6.2	Measurement Equipment Expenses
		2.2.6.3	Maintenance and Calibration Labor
2.2	Operations (Manufacturing or Service) Appraisal Costs	2.2.7	Outside Endorsements and Certifications
2.2.1	Planned Operations Inspections, Tests, Audits	2.3	External Appraisal Costs
		2.3.1	Field Performance Evaluation
2.2.1.1	Checking Labor	2.3.2	Special Product Evaluations
2.2.1.2	Product or Service Quality Audits	2.3.3	Evaluation of Field Stock and Spare Parts
2.2.1.3	Inspection and Test Materials		
2.2.2	Set-Up Inspections and Tests	2.4	Review of Test and Inspection Data
2.2.3	Special Tests (Manufacturing)	2.5	Miscellaneous Quality Evaluations

3.0	**INTERNAL FAILURE COSTS**		
3.1	Product/Service Design Failure Costs (Internal)	3.3.1	Material Review and Corrective Action Costs
3.1.1	Design Corrective Action	3.3.1.1	Disposition Costs
3.1.2	Rework Due to Design Changes	3.3.1.2	Troubleshooting or Failure Analysis Costs (Operations)
3.1.3	Scrap Due to Design Changes		
3.1.4	Production Liaison Costs	3.3.1.3	Investigation Support Costs
3.2	Purchasing Failure Costs	3.3.1.4	Operations Corrective Action 3.3.2 Operations Rework and Repair Costs
3.2.1	Purchased Material Reject Disposition Costs		
		3.3.2.1	Rework
3.2.2	Purchased material Replacement Costs	3.3.2.2	Repair
		3.3.2	Operations Rework and Repair Costs
3.2.3	Supplier Corrective Action	3.3.3	Re-inspection/Re-test Costs
3.2.4	Rework of Supplier Rejects	3.3.4	Extra Operations
3.2.5	Uncontrolled Material Losses	3.3.5	Scrap Costs (Operations)
3.3	Operations (Product or Service) Failure Costs	3.3.6	Downgraded End-Product or Service
		3.3.7	Internal Failure Labor Losses
		3.4	Other Internal Failure Costs

4.0	**EXTERNAL FAILURE COSTS**		
4.1	Complaint Investigations/Customer or User Service	4.5	Liability Costs
		4.6	Penalties
4.2	Returned Goods	4.7	Customer/User Goodwill
4.3	Retrofit Costs	4.8	Lost Sales
4.3.1	Recall Costs	4.9	Other External Failure Costs
4.4	Warranty Claims		

Figure B.1 Detailed quality cost element summary.

1.0 PREVENTION COSTS

Costs of all activities specifically designed to prevent poor quality in products or services.

1.1 Marketing/Customer/User

Costs incurred in the accumulation and continued evaluation of customer and user quality needs and perceptions (including feedback on reliability and performance) affecting their satisfaction with the company's product or service.

1.1.1 Marketing Research

The cost of that portion of marketing research devoted to the determination of customer and user quality needs—attributes of the product or service that provide a high degree of satisfaction.

1.1.2 Customer/User Perception Surveys/Clinics

The cost of programs designed to communicate with customers/users for the express purpose of determining their perception of product or service quality as delivered and used, from the viewpoint of their expectations and needs relative to competitive offerings.

1.1.3 Contract/Document Review

Costs incurred in the review and evaluation of customer contracts or other documents affecting actual product or service requirements (such as applicable industry standards, government regulations, or customer internal specifications) to determine the company's capability to meet the stated requirements, prior to acceptance of the customer's terms.

1.2 Product/Service/Design Development

Costs incurred to translate customer and user needs into reliable quality standards and requirements and manage the quality of new product or service developments prior to the release of authorized documentation for initial production. These costs are normally planned and budgeted and are applied to major design changes as well.

1.2.1 Design Quality Progress Reviews

The total cost, including planning, of interim and final design progress reviews, conducted to maximize conformance of product or service design to customer or user needs with regard to function, configuration, reliability, safety, produceability, unit cost, and as applicable, serviceability, inter-changeability, and maintainability. These formal reviews will occur prior to release of design documents for fabrication of prototype units or start of trial production.

1.2.2 Design Support Activities

The total cost of all activities specifically required to provide tangible quality support inputs to the product or service development effort. As applicable, design support activities include design document checking to assure conformance to internal design standards; selection and design qualification of components and/or materials required as an integral part of the end-product or service; risk analyses for the safe use of end-product or service; produceability studies to assure economic production capability; maintainability or serviceability analyses; reliability assurance activities such as failure mode and effects analysis and reliability apportionment; analysis of customer misuse and abuse potential; and preparation of an overall quality management plan.

1.2.3 Product Design Qualification Test

Costs incurred in the planning and conduct of the qualification testing of new products and major changes to existing products. Includes costs for the inspection and test of a sufficient quantity of qualification units under ambient conditions and the extremes of environmental parameters (worst case conditions). Qualification inspections and tests are conducted to verify that all product design requirements have been met or, when failures occur, to clearly identify where redesign efforts are required. Qualification testing is performed on prototype units, pilot runs, or a sample of the initial production run of new products. (Some sources consider this an appraisal cost.)

1.2.4 Service Design—Qualification

Costs incurred in the qualification or overall process proving of new service offerings and major changes to existing offerings. Involves planning for and performing a pilot or trial run using prototype or first production supplies as required. Includes detailed measurements or observations of each aspect of the service offering under normal and worst case conditions, for a sufficient quantity of units or time as applicable, to verify consistent conformance to requirements, or to identify where redesign efforts are required. (Some sources consider this an appraisal cost.)

1.2.5 Field Trials

The costs of planned observations and evaluation of end-product performance in trial situations—usually done with the cooperation of loyal customers but also includes sales into test markets. At this stage of product or service life, a company needs to know much more than "Did it work?" or "Did it sell?" (Some sources consider this an appraisal cost.)

1.3 Purchasing Prevention Costs

Costs incurred to assure conformance to requirements of supplier parts, materials, or processes and to minimize the impact of supplier nonconformances on the quality of delivered products or services. Involves activities prior to and after finalization of purchase order commitments.

1.3.1 Supplier Reviews

The total cost of surveys to review and evaluate individual supplier's capabilities to meet company quality requirements. Usually conducted by a team of qualified company representatives from affected departments. Can be conducted periodically for long-term associations.

1.3.2 Supplier Rating

The cost of developing and maintaining, as applicable, a system to ascertain each supplier's continued acceptability for future business. This rating system is based on actual supplier performance to established requirements, periodically analyzed, and given a quantitative or qualitative rating.

1.3.3 Purchase Order Tech Data Reviews

The cost for reviews of purchase order technical data (usually by other than purchasing personnel) to assure its ability to clearly and completely communicate accurate technical and quality requirements to suppliers.

1.3.4 Supplier Quality Planning

The total cost of planning for the incoming and source inspections and tests necessary to determine acceptance of supplier products. Includes the preparation of necessary documents and development costs for newly required inspection and test equipment.

1.4 Operations (Manufacturing or Service) Prevention Costs

Costs incurred in assuring the capability and readiness of operations to meet quality standards and requirements; quality control planning for all production activities; and the quality education of operating personnel.

1.4.1 Operations Process Validation

The cost of activities established for the purpose of assuring the capability of new production methods, processes, equipment, machinery, and tools to initially and consistently perform within required limits.

1.4.2 Operations Quality Planning

The total cost for development of necessary product or service inspection, test, and audit procedures; appraisal documentation systems; and workmanship or appearance standards to assure the continued achievement of acceptable quality results. Also includes total design and development costs for new or special measurement and control techniques, gauges, and equipment.

1.4.2.1 Design and Development of Quality Measurement and Control Equipment

The cost of test equipment, engineers, planners, and designers; gauge engineers; and inspection equipment engineers, planners, and designers.

1.4.3 Operations Support Quality Planning

The total cost of quality control planning for all activities required to provide tangible quality support to the production process. As applicable, these production support activities include, but are not limited to, preparation of specifications and the construction or purchase of new production equipment; preparation of operator instructions; scheduling and control plans for production supplies; laboratory analysis support; data processing support; and clerical support.

1.4.4 Operator Quality Education

Costs incurred in the development and conduct of formal operator training programs for the expressed purpose of preventing errors—programs that emphasize the value of quality and the role that each operator plays in its achievement. This includes operator training programs in subjects such as statistical quality control, process control, quality circles, and problem-solving techniques. This item is not intended to include any portion of basic apprentice or skill training necessary to be qualified for an individual assignment within a company.

1.4.5 Operator SPC/Process Control

Costs incurred for education to implement program.

1.5 Quality Administration

Costs incurred in the overall administration of the quality management function.

1.5.1 Administrative Salaries

Compensation costs for all quality function personnel such as managers and directors, supervisors, and clericals whose duties are 100% administrative.

1.5.2 Administrative Expenses

All other costs and expenses charged to or allocated to the quality management function not specifically covered elsewhere in this system (such as heat, light, telephone, and so on).

1.5.3 Quality Program Planning

The cost of quality (procedure) manual development and main-tenance, inputs to proposals, quality record keeping, strategic planning, and budget control.

1.5.4 Quality Performance Reporting

Costs incurred in quality performance data collection, compilation, analysis, and issuance in report forms designed to promote the continued improvement of quality performance Quality cost reporting would be included in this category.

1.5.5 Quality Education

Costs incurred in the initial (new employee indoctrination) and continued quality education of all company functions that can affect the quality of product or service as delivered to customers. Quality education programs emphasize the value of quality performance and the role that each function plays in its achievement.

1.5.6 Quality improvement

Costs incurred in the development and conduct of companywide quality improvement programs designed to promote awareness of improvement opportunities and provide unique individual opportunities for participation and contributions.

1.5.7 Quality System Audits

The cost of audits performed to observe and evaluate the overall effectiveness of the quality management system and procedures. Often accomplished by a team of management personnel. Auditing of product is an appraisal cost. (See 2.2.1.)

1.6 Other Prevention Costs

Represents all other expenses of the quality system, not previously covered, specifically designed to prevent poor quality of product or service.

2.0 APPRAISAL COSTS

Costs associated with measuring, evaluating, or auditing products or services to assure conformance to quality standards and performance requirements.

2.1 Purchasing Appraisal Costs

Purchasing appraisal costs generally can be considered to be the costs incurred for the inspection and/or test of purchased supplies or services to determine acceptability for use. These activities can be performed as part of a receiving inspection function or as a source inspection at the supplier's facility.

2.1.1 Receiving or Incoming Inspections and Tests

Total costs for all normal or routine inspection and/or test of purchased materials, products, and services. These costs represent the baseline costs of purchased goods appraisal as a continuing part of a normal receiving inspection function.

2.1.2 Measurement Equipment

The cost of acquisition (depreciation or expense costs), calibration, and maintenance of measurement equipment, instruments, and gauges used for appraisal of purchased supplies.

2.1.3 Qualification of Supplier Product

The cost of additional inspections or tests (including environmental tests) periodically required to qualify the use of production quantities of purchased goods. These costs are usually one-time costs but they may be repeated during multi-year production situations. The following are typical applications:

a. First article inspection (detailed inspection and worst-case tests) on a sample of the first production buy of new components, materials, or services.

b. First article inspection for second and third sources of previously qualified end-product key components.

c. First article inspection of the initial supply of customer-furnished parts or materials.

d. First article inspection of the initial purchased quantity of goods for resale.

2.1.4 Source inspection and Control Programs

All company-incurred costs (including travel) for the conduct of any of the activities described in 2.1.1 and 2.1.3 at the supplier's plant or at an independent test laboratory. This item will normally include all appraisal costs associated with direct shipments from supplier to the customer, sales office, or installation site.

2.2 Operations (Manufacturing or Service) Appraisal Costs

Operations appraisal costs generally can be considered to be the costs incurred for the inspections, tests, or audits required to determine and assure the acceptability of product or service to continue into each discrete step in the operations plan from start of production to delivery. In each case where material losses are an integral part of the appraisal operation, such as machine set-up pieces or destructive testing, the cost of the losses is to be included.

2.2.1 Planned Operations, Inspections, Tests, Audits

The cost of all planned inspections, tests, and audits conducted on product or service at selected points or work areas throughout the overall operations process including the point of final product or service acceptance Also includes the total cost of any destructive test samples required. This is the baseline operations appraisal cost. It does not include the cost of troubleshooting, rework, repair, or sorting rejected lots, all of which are defined as failure costs.

2.2.1.1 Checking Labor

Work performed by individuals other than inspectors as in-process evaluation. Typically part of a production operator's job.

2.2.1.2 Product or Service Quality Audits

Personnel expense as a result of performing quality audits on in-process or finished products or services.

2.2.1.3 Inspection and Test Materials

Materials consumed or destroyed in control of quality, e.g., by tear-down inspections, over-voltage stressing, drop testing, or life testing.

2.2.2 Set-Up Inspections and Tests

The cost of all set-up or first piece inspections and tests utilized to assure that each combination of machine and tool is properly adjusted to produce acceptable products before the start of each production lot, or that service processing equipment (including acceptance and test devices) is acceptable for the start of a new day, shift, or other time period.

2.2.3 Special Tests (Manufacturing)

The cost of all non routine inspections and tests conducted on manufactured product as a part of the appraisal plan. These costs normally include annual or semi-annual sampling of sensitive product for more detailed and extensive evaluations to assure continued conformance to critical environmental requirements.

2.2.4　Process Control Measurements

The cost of all planned measurements conducted on in-line product or service processing equipment and/or materials (e.g., oven temperature or material density) to assure conformance to pre-established standards. Includes adjustments made to maintain continued acceptable results.

2.2.5　Laboratory Support

The total cost of any laboratory tests required in support of product or service appraisal plans.

2.2.6　Measurement (Inspection and Test) Equipment

Since any measurement or process control equipment required is an integral part of appraisal operations, its acquisition (depreciation or expense), calibration, and maintenance costs are all included. Control of this equipment assures the integrity of results, without which the effectiveness of the appraisal program would be in jeopardy.

2.2.6.1　Depreciation Allowances

Total depreciation allowances for all capitalized appraisal equipment.

2.2.6.2　Measurement Equipment Expenses

The procurement or build cost of all appraisal equipment and gauges that are not capitalized.

2.2.6.3　Maintenance and Calibration Labor

The cost of all inspections, calibration, maintenance, and control of appraisal equipment, instruments, and gauges used for the evaluation of support processes, products, or services for conformance to requirements.

2.2.7　Outside Endorsements and Certifications

The total cost of required outside endorsements or certifications such as Underwriter's Laboratory, ASTM, or an agency of the U.S. government. Includes the cost of sample preparation, submittal, and any liaison necessary to its final achievement. Includes cost of liaison with customers.

2.3　External Appraisal Costs

External appraisal costs will be incurred any time there is need for field set-up or installation and checkout prior to official acceptance by the customer. These costs are also incurred when there is need for field trials of new products or services.

2.3.1 **Field Performance Evaluation**

The total cost of all appraisal efforts (inspections, tests, audits, and appraisal support activities) planned and conducted at the site for installation and/or delivery of large, complex products or the conduct of merchandised services (e.g., repairs or leasing set-ups).

2.3.2 **Special Product Evaluations**

Includes life testing and environmental and reliability tests performed on production units.

2.3.3 **Evaluation of Field Stock and Spare Parts**

Includes cost of evaluation testing or inspection of field stock, resulting from engineering changes, storage time (excessive shelf life), or other suspected problems.

2.4 Review of Test and Inspection Data

Costs incurred for regularly reviewing inspection and test data prior to release of the product for shipment, such as determining whether product requirements have been met.

2.5 Miscellaneous Quality Evaluations

The cost of all support area quality evaluations (audits) to assure continued ability to supply acceptable support to the production process. Examples of areas included are stores, packaging, and shipping.

3.0 INTERNAL FAILURE COSTS

Costs resulting from products or services not conforming to requirements or customer/user needs. Internal failure costs occur prior to delivery or shipment of the product, or the furnishing of a service, to the customer.

3.1 Product/Service Design Failure Costs (Internal)

Design failure costs can generally be considered to be the unplanned costs that are incurred because of inherent design inadequacies in released documentation for production operations. They do not include billable costs associated with customer-directed changes (product improvements) or major redesign efforts (product upgrading) that are part of a company-sponsored marketing plan.

3.1.1 **Design Corrective Action**

After initial release of design for production, the total cost of all problem investigation and redesign efforts (including requalification as necessary) required to completely resolve product or service problems inherent in the design. (Some sources consider this a prevention cost.)

3.1.2 Rework Due to Design Changes

The cost of all rework (materials, labor, and applicable burden) specifically required as part of design problem resolutions and implementation plan for required design changes.

3.1.3 Scrap Due to Design Changes

The cost of all scrap (materials, labor, and applicable burden) required as part of design problem resolutions and implementation plan for design changes.

3.1.4 Production Liaison Costs

The cost of unplanned production support efforts required because of inadequate or incomplete design description and documentation by the design organization.

3.2 Purchasing Failure Costs

Costs incurred due to purchased item rejects.

3.2.1 Purchased Material Reject Disposition Costs

The cost to dispose of, or sort, incoming inspection rejects. Includes the cost of reject documentation, review and evaluation, disposition orders, handling, and transportation (except as charged to the supplier).

3.2.2 Purchased Material Replacement Costs

The added cost of replacement for all items rejected and returned to supplier. Includes additional transportation and expediting costs (when not paid for by the supplier).

3.2.3 Supplier Corrective Action

The cost of company-sponsored failure analyses and investigations into the cause of supplier rejects to determine necessary corrective actions. Includes the cost of visits to supplier plants for this purpose and the cost to provide necessary added inspection protection while the problem is being resolved. (Some sources consider this a prevention cost.)

3.2.4 Rework of Supplier Rejects

The total cost of necessary supplier item repairs incurred by the company and not billable to the supplier—usually due to production expediencies.

3.2.5 Uncontrolled Material Losses

The cost of material or parts shortages due to damage, theft, or other (unknown) reasons. A measure of these costs may be obtained from reviews of inventory adjustments.

3.3 Operations (product or service) Failure Costs

Operations failure costs almost always represent a significant portion of overall quality costs and can generally be viewed as the costs associated with defective product or service discovered during the operations process. They are categorized into three distinct areas: material review and corrective action, rework/repair costs, and scrap costs.

3.3.1 Material Review and Corrective Action Costs

Costs incurred in the review and disposition of nonconforming product or service and the corrective actions necessary to prevent recurrence.

3.3.1.1 Disposition Costs

All costs incurred in the review and disposition of nonconforming product or service, in the analysis of quality data to determine significant areas for corrective action, and in the investigation of these areas to determine the root causes of the defective product or service.

3.3.1.2 Troubleshooting or Failure Analysis Costs (Operations)

The cost of failure analysis (physical or chemical) conducted by or obtained from outside laboratories in support of defect cause identification. (Some sources consider this a prevention cost.)

3.3.1.3 Investigation Support Costs

The additional cost of special runs of product or controlled lots of material (designed experiments) conducted specifically to obtain information useful to the determination of the root cause of a particular problem. (Some sources consider this a prevention cost.)

3.3.1.4 Operations Corrective Action

The actual cost of corrective actions taken to remove or eliminate the root causes of nonconformances identified for correction. This item can include such activities as rewriting operator instructions, redevelopment of specific processes or flow procedures, redesign or modification of equipment or tooling, and the development and implementation of specific training needs. Does not include design (3.1.1) or supplier (3.2.3) corrective action costs. (Some sources consider this a prevention cost.)

3.3.2 Operations Rework and Repair Costs

The total cost (labor, material, and overhead) of reworking or repairing defective product or service discovered within the operations process.

3.3.2.1 Rework

The total cost (material, labor, and burden) of all work done to bring nonconforming product or service up to an acceptable (conforming) condition, as authorized by specific work order, blueprint, personal assignment, or a planned part of the standard operating process. Does not include rework due to design change (3.1.2).

3.3.2.2 Repair

The total cost (material, labor, and burden) of all work done to bring non-conforming product up to an acceptable or equivalent, but still non-conforming, condition; normally accomplished by subjecting the product to an approved process that will reduce but not completely eliminate the nonconformance.

3.3.3 Re-inspection/Re-test Costs

That portion of inspection, test, and audit labor that is incurred because of rejects (includes documentation of rejects, re-inspection or test after re-work/repair, and sorting of defective lots).

3.3.4 Extra Operations

The total cost of extra operations such as touch-up or trimming, added because the basic operation is not able to achieve conformance to requirements. These costs are often hidden in the accepted (standard) cost of operations.

3.3.5 Operations Scrap Costs

The total cost (material, labor, and overhead) of defective product or service that is wasted or disposed of because it cannot be reworked to conform to requirements. The unavoidable losses of material (such as the turnings from machining work or the residue in a food mixing pot) are generally known as waste (check company cost accounting definitions) and are not to be included in the cost of quality Also, in the definition of quality costs, the amount received from the sale of scrap and waste material (salvage value) is not to be deducted from gross scrap failure costs.

3.3.6 Downgraded End-Product or Service

Price differential between normal selling price and reduced selling price due to nonconforming or off-grade end-products or services because of quality reasons. Also includes any costs incurred to bring up to saleable condition.

3.3.7 Internal Failure Labor Losses

When labor is lost because of nonconforming work, there may be no concurrent material losses and it is not reflected on scrap or rework reports. Accounting for the cost of labor for such losses is the intent of this item. Typical losses occur because of equipment shutdowns and reset-up or line stoppages for quality reasons and may be efficiency losses or even allocated for by "labor allowances."

3.4 Other Internal Failure Costs

4.0 EXTERNAL FAILURE COSTS

Costs resulting from products or services not conforming to requirements or customer / user needs. External failure costs occur after delivery or shipment of the product, and during or after furnishing of a service, to the customer.

4.1 Complaint Investigations/Customer or User Service

The total cost of investigating, resolving, and responding to individual customer or user complaints or inquiries, including necessary field service.

4.2 Returned Goods

The total cost of evaluating and repairing or replacing goods not meeting acceptance by the customer or user due to quality problems. It does not include repairs accomplished as part of a maintenance or modification contract.

4.3 Retrofit Costs

Costs to modify or update products or field service facilities to a new design change level based on major redesign due to design deficiencies. Includes only that portion of retrofits that are due to quality problems.

4.3.1 Recall Costs

Includes costs of recall activity due to quality problems.

4.4 Warranty Claims

The total cost of claims paid to the customer or user, after acceptance, to cover expenses. Includes repair costs such as removing defective hardware from a system or cleaning costs due to a food or chemical service accident. In cases where a price reduction is negotiated in lieu of warranty, the value of this reduction should be counted.

4.5 Liability Costs

Company-paid costs due to liability claims, including the cost of product or service liability insurance.

4.6 Penalties

Cost of any penalties incurred because of less than full product or service performance achieved (as required by contracts with customers and government rules and regulations).

4.7 Customer/User Goodwill

Costs incurred, over and above normal selling costs, to customers or users who are not completely satisfied with the quality of delivered product or service. Includes costs incurred because customer quality expectations are greater than product or service received.

4.8 Lost Sales

Includes value of contribution margin lost due to sales reduction because of quality problems. (These costs should be clearly and directly related to specific instances of poor quality, not surmised or assumed to be vaguely related to prior issues.)

4.9 Other External Failure Costs

Appendix C
Bibliography of Publications and Papers Relating to Quality Costs

The papers and publications included below are those that, in the opinion of the editor and support team, have significantly contributed to the field of quality costs. Most papers on the subject (written through 1987) can be found in *Quality Costs—Ideas and Applications*, referenced below.

ASQC Quality Costs Committee. *Guide for Managing Supplier Quality Costs.* Edited by W.O. Winchell. Milwaukee: ASQC Quality Press, 1986.

ASQC Quality Costs Committee. *Guide for Reducing Quality Costs.* Milwaukee: ASQC Quality Press, 1986.

ASQC Quality Costs Committee. *Quality Costs What and How.* Milwaukee: ASQC Quality Press, 1974.

ASQC Quality Costs Committee. *Quality Costs Ideas and Applications, Volumes 1 and 2.* Edited by Jack Campanella. Milwaukee: ASQC Quality Press, 1987 and 1989, respectively.

Atkinson, Hawley, John Hamburg, and Christopher Ittner. *Linking Quality to Profits.* Milwaukee: ASQC Quality Press and Montvale, NJ: Institute of Management Accountants, 1994.

Atkinson, John Hawley Jr., Gregory Hohner, Barry Mundt, Richard B. Troxel, and William Winchell. *Current Trends in Cost of Quality: Linking the Cost of Quality and Continuous Improvement.* Montvale, NJ: National Association of Accountants, 1991.

Campanella, Jack and Frank J. Corcoran. "Principles of Quality Costs." *Quality Progress* 16, No. 4 (1983): 16–22.

Campanella, Jack and Frank J. Corcoran. "Principles of Quality Costs." In *Annual Quality Congress Transactions.* Milwaukee: American Society for Quality Control, 1982.

Corcoran, Frank J. "Quality Costs Principles—A Preview." In *Annual Technical Conferences Transactions*. Milwaukee: American Society for Quality Control, 1980.

Crosby, P. *Quality is Free*. New York: McGraw-Hill Book Company, 1979.

Feigenbaum, Armand V. *Total Quality Control*, 3rd edition, Chapter 7. New York: McGraw-Hill Book Company, 1983.

Freeman, H. L. "How to Put Quality Costs to Work." Paper presented at 12th Metropolitan Section All Day Conference, 1960.

Harrington, H. J. *Poor Quality Costs*. Milwaukee: ASQC Quality Press, 1986.

Juran, J.M. and Frank M. Gryna. *Juran's Quality Control Handbook*, 4th edition, Chapter 4. New York: McGraw-Hill Book Company, 1988.

Juran, J. M. and Frank M. Gryna. *Quality Planning and Analysis*, 3rd edition, New York: McGraw-Hill Book Company, 1993.

Masser, W. J. "The Quality Manager and Quality Costs." *Industrial Quality Control* 14, (1957): 5–8.

Morse, Wayne J., Kay M. Poston, and Harold P. Roth. *Measuring and Controlling Quality Costs*. Montvale, NJ: National Association of Accountants, 1987.

Ross, Louise and Ivan Kovachev. *Management Accounting Tools for Today and Tomorrow*, Chartered Institute of Management Accountants, July 2009, www.cimaglobal.com/Thought-leadership/Research-topics/Management-accounting-in-different-sectors/Management-accounting-survey/

Schiffauerova, A. and V. Thomson, "Managing cost of quality: Insight into industry practice", *The TQM Magazine*, 2006.

Williams, R. J. "Guide for Reducing Quality Costs." In *Annual Quality Congress Transactions*. Milwaukee: American Society for Quality Control, 1982.

Winchell, William O. "Guide for Managing Vendor Quality Costs." In *Annual Quality Congress Transactions*. Milwaukee: American Society for Quality Control, 1981.

Wood, Dogulas C. "Expert Answers" In *Quality Progress*. January 2012. www.asq.org/quality-progress/2012/01/expert-answers.html

References

CHAPTER 1

1. "The National Conference for Quality." *Quality Progress* 15, No. 5 (May 1952): 14–17.

2. Harrington, H. J. *Poor-Quality Cost.* Milwaukee: ASQC Quality Press, 1987.

3. Juran, J. M. and Frank M. Gryna. "Section 4, Quality Costs." *Juran's Quality Control Handbook,* 4th ed. New York: McGraw-Hill Book Company, 1988.

4. MIL-Q-9858A, *Quality Program Requirements.* Department of Defense, 1963.

5. Brown, F.X. and R. W. Kane. "Quality Costs and Profit Performance" *Annual Technical Conference Transactions.* Milwaukee: American Society for Quality Control, 1975.

6. Dawes, Edgar W. *"Quality Costs—New Concepts and Methods."* Annual Quality Congress Transactions Milwaukee: American Society for Quality Control, 1987.

7. Byrne, Diane M. and Nancy E. Ryan, eds. *Taguchi Methods and QFD.* Dearborn, Mich.: ASI Press, 1988.

8. Eureka, William E. and Nancy E. Ryan, eds. *The Customer-Driven Company.* Dearborn, Mich.: ASI Press, 1988.

9. Ealey, Lance A. *Quality by Design.* Dearborn, Mich.: ASI Press, 1988.

10. ANSI/ASQC Q9004-1-1994, *Quality Management and Quality System Elements—Guidelines* (Milwaukee: ASQC Quality Press, 1994) 7–8.

11. ANSI/ASQC ISO/DIS10014, *Guidelines for Managing the Economics of Quality—Draft International Standard,* 1996.

12. QS-9000, *Quality System Requirements.* 3rd ed., March 1998.

13. International Organization for Standardization, ISO 9001:2008, *Quality management systems—Requirements,* The International Organization for Standardization, Geneva, Switzerland, November 15, 2008.

14. International Organization for Standardization, ISO 9004:2009, *Quality management systems—Managing for sustained success of an organization,* The International Organization for Standardization, Geneva, Switzerland, 2009.

15. ISO 9001:2000, the *Quality Management Forum,* Winter 2006, Pages 7–9.

16. ISO 10014:2006. *Quality management—Guidelines for realizing financial and economic benefits,* The International Organization for Standardization, Geneva, Switzerland, November 1, 2006.

17. *TL 9000 Requirements Handbook,* Release 5.0, November 15, 2009 and *TL 9000 Measurements Handbook,* Release 4.5, July 1, 2010. QuEST Forum, Plano, TX.

18. ISO 9000:2005. *Quality management systems—Fundamentals and vocabulary.* The International Organization for Standardization, Geneva, Switzerland, 2005.

19. *TL 9000 Requirements Handbook,* Release 5.0, November 15, 2009, QuEST Forum, Plano, TX.

20. *TL 9000 Measurements,* Release 4.5, July 1, 2010. QuEST Forum, Plano, TX.

21. Liebesman, Sandford, Alka Jarvis, and Ashok V. Dandekar. *TL 9000, Release 3.0, and a Guide to Measuring Excellence in Telecommunications,* Second Edition. Milwaukee: ASQ Quality Press, 2002.

22. Liebesman, Sandford, "TL 9000: The Telecommunications Quality Management System," Chapter 60 in *The ASQ ISO 9000:2000 Handbook,* eds. Charles A. Cianfrani, Joseph J. Tsiakals and John E. (Jack) West. Milwaukee: ASQ Quality Press, 2002, 819–842.

23. Liebesman, Sandford and John Walz, "New Version of TL 9000 Released," Standards Outlook, *Quality Progress,* March 2007, 74–76.

24. Liebesman, Sandford. "Increase ISO 9001's Value," *Quality Progress,* August 2006, 84–85.

25. Liebesman, Sandford. "Continual Improvement using ISO 9001," *Quality Progress,* January 2003, 62–63.

CHAPTER 2

1. Campanella, Jack and Frank J. Corcoran. "Principles of Quality Costs." In *Annual Quality Congress Transactions*. Milwaukee: American Society for Quality Control, 1982.

CHAPTER 3

1. Krause, J.D. and Frank M. Gryna. *Activity Based Costing and Cost of Poor Quality — A Partnership*, University of Tampa Report No. 109, 1995.

2. Atkinson, J.H., G. Hohner, B. Mundt, R. B. Troxel, and W. Winchell, *Current Trends in Cost of Quality*, National Association of Accountants Publication No. 91259, Montvale, N.J., 1991.

3. Campanella, J. 1990. *Principles of Quality Costs*, 2nd. ed., Milwaukee: ASQC Quality Press.

4. Webster, D.W. *Achieving Value Through Activity-Based Costing*, Proceedings of ASQC 49th Annual Quality Congress, Cincinnati, Ohio, 1995.

CHAPTER 4

1. Briscoe, Nat R. and Frank M. Gryna. *Assessing the Cost of Poor Quality in a Small Business*, The University of Tampa College of Business. Report No. 902, May 1996. Also published in *Qimpro Quarterly*, India, 1998.

2. Juran, J. M. and Frank M. Gryna. *Quality Planning and Analysis*, 3rd ed., New York: McGraw-Hill Book Company, 1993.

3. Juran, J.M. and Frank M. Gryna. "Section 22, Quality Improvement." *Juran's Quality Control Handbook*, 4th ed., New York: McGraw-Hill Book Company, 1988.

4. ASQ Quality Costs Committee. *Guide for Reducing Quality Costs*. Milwaukee: ASQC Quality Press, 1987.

5. ASQ Quality Costs Committee. *Guide for Managing Supplier Quality Costs*, 2nd ed.. Milwaukee: ASQC Quality Press, 1887.

6. Knox, S.T. "Modeling the Cost of Software Quality," *Digital Technical Journal*, 5(4), 9–16 (Fall 1993).

7. Dion, R. Process Improvement and the Corporate Balance Sheet, *IEEE Software*, 10(July), 28–35 (1993).

8. Haley, T.J. Software Process Improvement at Raytheon, *IEEE Software*, 13(November), 33–41 (1996).

9. Paulk, Mark C., Bill Curtis, Mary Beth Chrissis, and Charles V. Weber. *Capability Maturity Model for Software,* Version 1.1 (CMU/SEI-93-TR-25), Software Engineering Institute, Carnegie Mellon University, Pittsburgh, Pennsylvania (1993).

10. Weller, E.F.. "Lessons from Three Years of Inspection Data," *IEEE Software,* (September), 38–45 (1993).

11. Pressman, Roger S. *Software engineering: a practitioner's approach,* 6th ed., McGraw-Hill, 2005.

12. Gack, Gary. "Powerful Metrics: Software Cost of Quality + Defect Containment," *Software Quality Professional,* Volume 13, Issue Two, (March 2011), 5–8.

13. Mahanti, Rupa. "Software Six Sigma and Cultural Change: The Key Ingredients," *Software Quality Professional,* Volume 13, Issue Two, (March 2011), 43–45.

14. Jones, Capers. "Software Quality and Software Costs," *Software Quality Professional,* Volume 13, Issue Three, (June 2011), 28–29.

15. Phillips, Jack. "Valuing Quality Initiatives: New Perspectives for Measuring Success with Six Types of Data," *The Quality Management Forum,* Volume 34, Number 8 (Fall 2008), 21–24.

16. Lofgren, M. and L. Witell. "Two Decades of Using Kano's Theory of Attractive Quality: A Literature Review," *ASQ Quality Management Journal,* Volume 15, Issue 1 (2008), 61–64.

17. Kristensen, K. and J. Eskildsen. "The Relationship Between SERVQUAL, National Customer Satisfaction Indices, and Consumer Sentiment," *ASQ Quality Management Journal,* Volume 19, Issue 2 (2012), 50–55.

18. Futrell, R., D. Shafer, and L. Shafer. *Quality Software Project Management,* Prentice Hall PTR, 2002.

19. ASQ CSQE BOK. www.prdweb.asq.org/certification/control/software-quality-engineer/bok.

20. Brodman, J. and D. Johnson. 1996. "Return on investment from software process improvement as measured by U.S. industry." CrossTalk, *Journal of Defense Software Engineering.* 9 (4), 23–28.

21. Karg, Lars M., Michael Grottke, and Arne Beckhaus, "A systematic literature review of software quality cost research," *Journal of Systems and Software,* Volume 84, Issue 3, March 2011, Pages 415–427.

22. Slaughter, Sandra A., Donald E. Harter, and Mayuram S. Krishnan. "Evaluating the cost of software quality." *Communications of the ACM 41,* 8, 1998, 67-73.

23. van Solingen, Rini. "Measuring the ROI of Software Process Improvement." *IEEE Software* 21, 3. 2004, 32–38.

CHAPTER 5

1. ASQ Quality Costs Committee. *Guide for Reducing Quality Costs,* 2nd ed. Milwaukee: ASQC Quality Press, 1987.

2. Atkinson, John Hawley Jr.; Gregory Hohner; Barry Mundt; Richard B. Troxel; and William Winchell. *Current Trends in Cost of Quality: Linking the Cost of Quality and Continuous Improvement.* Montvale, NJ: National Association of Accountants, 1991.

3. Quality Cost Committee. *Principles of Quality Costs,* 2nd ed., Campanella, Jack, Editor. Milwaukee: ASQC Quality Press, 1990.

4. Juran, J. M. and Frank M. Gryna. *Quality Planning and Analysis: From Product Development through Use,* 3rd ed., New York: McGraw-Hill, Inc., 1993.

5. Newnan, Donald G. *Engineering Economic Analysis,* 4th ed., San Jose: Engineering Press, Inc. 1991.

6. Winchell, William. *Continuous Quality Improvement: A Manufacturing Professionals Guide,* Dearborn: Society of Manufacturing Engineers, 1991.

7. Winchell, William. "Driving Buyer Satisfaction by Quality Cost." *50th Annual Quality Congress Transactions.* Milwaukee: American Society for Quality Control, 1996.

CHAPTER 6

1. Dion, R. "Quantifying the Benefit of Software Process Improvement," Proceedings of the SEI/AIAA Software Process Improvement Workshop, November 8, 1990, Chantilly, VA.

2. Dion, R. "Cost of Quality as a Measure of Process Improvement," Proceedings of the SEI Software Engineering Symposium, Sept. 17, 1992.

3. Dion, R. "Process Improvement and the Corporate Balance Sheet," *IEEE Software*, Vol. 10, No. 4, July 1993, pp. 28–35.

4. Haley, T., B. Ireland, E. Wojtaszek, D. Nash, and R. Dion, "Raytheon Electronic Systems Experience in Software Process Improvement," Technical Report CMU/SEI-95-TR-017, November, 1995

5. Haley, T. "Software Process Improvement at Raytheon," *IEEE Software*, Vo. 13, No. 6, November, 1996, pp 33–41.

6. Krasner, H. "Accumulating the Body of Evidence for the Payoff of SPI," 1997, see www.utexas.edu/coe/sqi/archive.

7. Pressman, Roger S. *Software engineering: a practitioner's approach*, 6th ed. McGraw-Hill, 2005.

8. Gack, Gary. "Powerful Metrics: Software Cost of Quality + Defect Containment," *Software Quality Professional*, Volume 13, Issue Two (March 2011), 5–8.

9. Mahanti, Rupa. "Software Six Sigma and Cultural Change: The Key Ingredients," *Software Quality Professional*, Volume 13, Issue Two (March 2011), 43–45.

10. Jones, Capers. "Software Quality and Software Costs," *Software Quality Professional*, Volume 13, Issue Three (June 2011), 28–29.

11. Phillips, Jack. "Valuing Quality Initiatives: New Perspectives for Measuring Success with Six Types of Data," The Quality Management Forum, Volume 34, Number 8 (Fall 2008), 21–24.

12. Lofgren, M. and L. Witell. "Two Decades of Using Kano's Theory of Attractive Quality: A Literature Review," *ASQ Quality Management Journal*, Volume 15, Issue 1 (2008), 61–64.

13. Kristensen, K. and J. Eskildsen. "The Relationship Between SERVQUAL, National Customer Satisfaction Indices, and Consumer Sentiment, *ASQ Quality Management Journal*, Volume 19, Issue 2 (2012), 50–55.

14. Futrell, R., D. Shafer, and L. Shafer. *Quality Software Project Management*, New York: Prentice Hall PTR, 2002.

About the Authors

EDITOR

Douglas C. Wood has been in private consulting since 2007, working with a diverse set of industrial and medical clients on quality improvement, quality assurance, and measurement. His work experience spans 35 years, including Kellogg Co. and Hallmark Cards, Inc. He has taught more than 100 classes in lean, Six Sigma, statistics, root cause analysis, measurement, and cost of quality both in person and in virtual settings. He holds three American Society for Quality (ASQ) certifications—Six Sigma Black Belt, CQE, and CMQ/OE—and is certified in lean with the Society of Manufacturing Engineers. He has been an examiner with the Kansas and Missouri state quality award programs. He is a trained industrial engineer (Western Michigan University BSIE 1978) and a lifelong student of psychology. Wood is also a past chair of the ASQ Quality Cost Committee, and authored *The Executive Guide to Understanding and Implementing Quality Cost Programs*, published by ASQ Quality Press in 2007. His website is www.dcwoodconsulting.com.

CONTRIBUTORS

Taz Daughtrey is senior software quality scientist at the Cyber Security and Information Systems Information Analysis Center. He has been a member of the computer science faculty at James Madison University since 2001. Taz is a fellow of the American Society for Quality, the founding editor of the peer-reviewed journal *Software Quality Professional*, and a director of the American Software Testing Qualifications Board. His previous 20 years in industry included responsibilities as quality manager and chief security officer, and he held a number of roles in software development, training, and quality improvement in commercial and naval nuclear manufacturing and engineering.

Gary Cokins is an internationally recognized expert, speaker, blogger, and book author in advanced cost management and performance improvement systems. He is the founder of Analytics-Based Performance Management, an advisory firm in Cary, North Carolina. His website is www.garycokins.com. Gary received a BS degree with honors in Industrial Engineering/Operations

Research from Cornell University in 1971. He received his MBA from Northwestern University's Kellogg School of Management in 1974. Gary began his career as a strategic planner with FMC's Link-Belt Division and then served as financial controller and operations manager. In 1981 Gary began his management consulting career with Deloitte Consulting. At KPMG (1988), he was trained on activity-based cost management (ABC) by Harvard Business School professors Robert S. Kaplan and Robin Cooper. In 1992 Gary headed the National Cost Management Consulting Services for Electronic Data Systems (EDS), now part of HP. From 1997 until recently, Gary was in business development with SAS, a provider of enterprise performance management and business analytics and intelligence software.

Gary has authored six books including *Activity Based Cost Management: An Executive's Guide, Performance Management: Finding the Missing Pieces to Close the Intelligence Gap,* and *Performance Management: Integrating Strategy Execution, Methodologies, Risk, and Analytics.*

Gary also participates and serves on committees including: The AICPA, CAM-I, the American Association of Accountants (AAA), the International Federation of Accountants (IFAC), the Supply Chain Council, and the Institute of Management Accountants (IMA).

Dr. Sandford Liebesman, Sandford Quality Consulting LLC and retired corporate ISO manager at Lucent Technologies, Inc., had more than 43 years of experience in quality at Bell Laboratories, Lucent Technologies, Bellcore (Telcordia), and KEMA Registered Quality. He is an ISO 9000 subject matter expert and auditor and is author of the books *Competitive Advantage: Linked Management Systems, TL 9000, Release 3.0: A Guide to Measuring Excellence in Telecommunications, 2nd Edition,* and *Using ISO 9000 to Improve Business Processes.* He has presented seminars and published articles on linking management systems and QMS/EMS support of Sarbanes-Oxley and he led the team that developed the 2005 and 2006 ASQ SOX conferences. He has conducted more than 95 registrar audits of ISO 9001 and TL 9000 and he also conducted internal audits as a member of Lucent Technologies. Dr. Liebesman has an engineering degree from the United States Naval Academy and MSEE and Ph.D. (Operations Research) degrees from New York University. He taught statistics, quality control, quality management, and operations research at Rutgers University. He is the past chair of the ASQ Electronics and Communications Division and a fellow of ASQ.

Daniel Zrymiak is from Surrey, British Columbia, Canada, where he lives with his wife Susan and children Ryan and Brooke. Daniel brings more than 20 years of professional experience in quality management. He currently leads mobilization and delivery management programs for software outsourcing clients at Accenture. Prior to joining Accenture several years ago, Daniel worked in Hong Kong, Germany, and Canada in business services, manufacturing, medical software, and web commerce solutions. Daniel was also a part-time faculty member at the University of British Columbia, British Columbia Institute of Technology, and Kwantlen Polytechnic University where he taught software quality assurance, software testing, statistics, and configuration management. Daniel has attained fellow membership in ASQ, associate membership in the International Academy for Quality, recognition with ASQ's Feigenbaum Medal and Testimonial Award, and multiple certifications including Six Sigma Black Belt, CQM/OE, Certified Software Quality Engineer, and Certified Quality Engineer. He has lead auditor credentials and he has been a conference speaker at numerous international quality conferences. Daniel is active in the American Society for Quality as an ASQ Quality Press author and reviewer, member-leader, and committee chair.

Jd Marhevko is currently the vice president of Quality and Lean for Accuride Corp. She has been involved in operations and Lean–Six Sigma efforts for more than 25 years across a variety of industries. Jd holds four American Society for Quality (ASQ) certifications—ASQ Fellow, CMQ/OE, CQE, and CSSBB—and she is an ASQ certified trainer for a variety of quality sciences. Jd is an MBB and has held various MBNQA assessor roles. She has trained more than 1000 Six Sigma Black Belts. She was an IRCA QSA for more than 10 years. She holds a BSE from Oakland University in Michigan and an MSA from Central Michigan University. Jd is the immediate past-chair of the ASQ QMD. With her husband, Mark Druckmiller, Jd co-authored the book *A Sample Size of One,* detailing the application of DMAIC and lean techniques with their son, Adam, who is on the autism spectrum.

Index

Page numbers in *italics* refer to figures or tables.

The Knowledge Center
www.asq.org/knowledge-center

Learn about quality. Apply it. Share it.

ASQ's online Knowledge Center is the place to:

- Stay on top of the latest in quality with Editor's Picks and Hot Topics.

- Search ASQ's collection of articles, books, tools, training, and more.

- Connect with ASQ staff for personalized help hunting down the knowledge you need, the networking opportunities that will keep your career and organization moving forward, and the publishing opportunities that are the best fit for you.

Use the Knowledge Center Search to quickly sort through hundreds of books, articles, and other software-related publications.

www.asq.org/knowledge-center

Ask a Librarian

Did you know?

- The ASQ Quality Information Center contains a wealth of knowledge and information available to ASQ members and non-members

- A librarian is available to answer research requests using ASQ's ever-expanding library of relevant, credible quality resources, including journals, conference proceedings, case studies and Quality Press publications

- ASQ members receive free internal information searches and reduced rates for article purchases

- You can also contact the Quality Information Center to request permission to reuse or reprint ASQ copyrighted material, including journal articles and book excerpts

- For more information or to submit a question, visit **http://asq.org/knowledge-center/ask-a-librarian-index**

Visit www.asq.org/qic for more information.

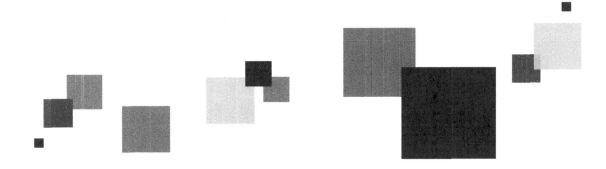

Belong to the Quality Community!

Established in 1946, ASQ is a global community of quality experts in all fields and industries. ASQ is dedicated to the promotion and advancement of quality tools, principles, and practices in the workplace and in the community.

The Society also serves as an advocate for quality. Its members have informed and advised the U.S. Congress, government agencies, state legislatures, and other groups and individuals worldwide on quality-related topics.

Vision

By making quality a global priority, an organizational imperative, and a personal ethic, ASQ becomes the community of choice for everyone who seeks quality technology, concepts, or tools to improve themselves and their world.

ASQ is...

- More than 90,000 individuals and 700 companies in more than 100 countries

- The world's largest organization dedicated to promoting quality

- A community of professionals striving to bring quality to their work and their lives

- The administrator of the Malcolm Baldrige National Quality Award

- A supporter of quality in all sectors including manufacturing, service, healthcare, government, and education

- YOU

Visit www.asq.org for more information.

TRAINING CERTIFICATION CONFERENCES MEMBERSHIP **PUBLICATIONS**

ASQ Membership

Research shows that people who join associations experience increased job satisfaction, earn more, and are generally happier*. ASQ membership can help you achieve this while providing the tools you need to be successful in your industry and to distinguish yourself from your competition. So why wouldn't you want to be a part of ASQ?

Networking

Have the opportunity to meet, communicate, and collaborate with your peers within the quality community through conferences and local ASQ section meetings, ASQ forums or divisions, ASQ Communities of Quality discussion boards, and more.

Professional Development

Access a wide variety of professional development tools such as books, training, and certifications at a discounted price. Also, ASQ certifications and the ASQ Career Center help enhance your quality knowledge and take your career to the next level.

Solutions

Find answers to all your quality problems, big and small, with ASQ's Knowledge Center, mentoring program, various e-newsletters, *Quality Progress* magazine, and industry-specific products.

Access to Information

Learn classic and current quality principles and theories in ASQ's Quality Information Center (QIC), *ASQ Weekly* e-newsletter, and product offerings.

Advocacy Programs

ASQ helps create a better community, government, and world through initiatives that include social responsibility, Washington advocacy, and Community Good Works.

Visit www.asq.org/membership for more information on ASQ membership.

*2008, The William E. Smith Institute for Association Research

TRAINING CERTIFICATION CONFERENCES MEMBERSHIP **PUBLICATIONS**

The Global Voice of Quality™